TIMSS MONOGRAPH NO. 3

Mathematics Textbooks:
A Comparative Study of Grade 8 Texts

Geoffrey Howson

GENERAL EDITOR, DAVID F. ROBITAILLE

PACIFIC EDUCATIONAL PRESS
VANCOUVER   CANADA

Published by Pacific Educational Press
Faculty of Education
University of British Columbia
Vancouver, Canada V6T 1Z4
Telephone: (604) 822-5385
Fax: (604) 822-6603
e-mail: cedwards@unixg.ubc.ca

The publisher would like to acknowlege the financial support provided by Heritage Canada for its publishing program.

Canadian Cataloguing in Publication Data
Howson, A. G. (Albert Geoffrey), 1931-
  Mathematics textbooks

  (TIMSS monograph ; no. 3)
  Includes bibliographical references and index.
  ISBN 1-895766-03-6

  1. Mathematics--Study and teaching (Secondary) I. Title. II. Series.
QA11.H68 1995   510'.71'2   C95-910260-4

Editing: Carolyn Sale
Design: Warren Clark
Printed and bound in Canada

10 9 8 7 6 5 4 3 2 1

Contents

Acknowledgements

Author's Acknowledgements

I should like to express my gratitude to all the TIMSS National Research Co-ordinators who supplied me with the texts used in this study and to David Robitaille and Bill Schmidt for their encouragement and aid. I am also much indebted to Beverley Maxwell and Carolyn Sale for their help in the preparation of this book. Finally, I am most grateful to all the textbook authors who provided the stimulus for this work. I hope that they do not feel that I have been unduly critical of their efforts. Certainly, there was no book from which I did not receive new ideas on the presentation of mathematics or the construction of exercises. Indeed, on re-reading the detailed comments I had made on the various texts, I was reminded how many times I had remarked upon an outstanding section or a particularly interesting or novel example. As a former textbook editor, I am aware of the errors and misjudgements that immediately strike one as soon as a book is in print and it is too late to do anything about it, and also of the great constraints that are imposed upon authors. Despite the criticisms, textbook authors must realize that theirs is one of the most important tasks within mathematics education

—Geoffrey Howson

Acknowledgements by TIMSS

Financial support for the International Coordinating Centre for TIMSS (University of British Columbia, Canada) is being provided by: Employment & Immigration Canada; Industry, Science & Technology Canada; and the British Columbia Ministry of Education. Financial support for the TIMSS Study Center (Boston College, U.S.A.) is being provided by the National Center for Educational Statistics, U.S. Department of Education, the U.S. National Science Foundation; and the International Association for the Evaluation of Educational Achievement (IEA). TIMSS would also like to thank Tor Virding of Vancouver and Svein Lie of the University of Oslo, Norway for their assistance translating examples from the Norwegian textbook.

Foreword

In this third monograph issued by the Third International Mathematics and Science Study (TIMSS), Geoffrey Howson presents his analysis of mathematics textbooks for 13-year-old students from eight of the countries participating in the study. Professor Howson has been involved with TIMSS since the outset, initially as a member of the International Steering Committee, and later as a member of the Subject Matter Advisory Committee.

This monograph is based on research originally commissioned as part of the Survey of Mathematics and Science Opportunity (SMSO), and we are indebted to Bill Schmidt, director of SMSO, for the support of this research and its contribution to the TIMSS monograph series. The SMSO project was designed to develop questionnaires and other instrumentation for use in TIMSS, with a particular focus on developing better ways to assess the opportunity-to-learn variable in mathematics and science at the classroom level. This included collecting textbooks, curriculum guides, pedagogical information, and descriptions of the educational system from each country. Six of the countries which were to participate in TIMSS agreed to take part in SMSO as well. They were France, Japan, Norway, Spain, Switzerland, and the United States. The textbooks of these countries, the United Kingdom, and the Netherlands are the subject of this monograph.

Professor Howson's analysis provides valuable ideas and examples for a number of important areas of mathematics education: research on textbooks, the role of the textbook and the teacher, textbook design, the pedagogical and philosophical orientation of the textbook, and many aspects of the mathematics content of the books studied. In addition to educational researchers, this monograph will be of particular interest to mathematics educators curious about the mathematics taught in other countries and the approaches that are used.

In every country, mathematics textbooks exert a considerable influence on the teaching and learning of mathematics, so an understanding of how textbooks vary in their content and approach across countries is an important area of investigation. In so doing, however, some caution must be exercised since we have little or no information about how these, or any other, textbooks actually influence what transpires in mathematics classrooms.

In the conceptual framework for TIMSS, we differentiate among the intended curriculum, the implemented curriculum, and the attained curriculum. This raises questions about the role and function of mathematics textbooks. In most places, the textbook is almost certainly not the embodiment of the intended curriculum. More likely, and as Professor Howson's analysis indicates, the textbook is either a subset or a superset of the intended curriculum. Similarly, the textbook is not identical to the implemented curriculum, as teachers make their own decisions about which topics to include or not to include in their course, and about which approach or approaches to take in the teaching of particular topics. An analysis of textbooks makes an important contribution to understanding curricula in a particular country, but this is a necessary, not a sufficient, condition for that understanding to be possible.

As General Editor of the TIMSS monograph series I am pleased to announce that we have established an Editorial Board. The membership is drawn from the three fields most closely associated with TIMSS: namely, mathematics education, science education, and research methodology in education. The three mathematics educators on the board are Ken Travers of the University of Illinois at Urbana-Champaign, Reverend Ben Nebres of the Ateneo de Manila University, and me. The science educators are Paul Black of King's College, London, Theo Wubbels of the University of Utrecht, and Svein Lie of the University of Oslo. The methodologists are Judith Torney-Purta of the University of Maryland and Al Beaton, the TIMSS Study Director, of Boston College. Beverley Maxwell and Ed Robeck, from the International Coordinating Centre, provide research and editorial support.

David F. Robitaille
International Coordinator for TIMSS
Vancouver, 1995

Preface

The Survey of Mathematics and Science Opportunity (SMSO) was designed to develop better opportunity-to-learn methodology for the Third International Mathematics and Science Study (TIMSS), as well as to characterize the educational opportunities for learning mathematics and science in the SMSO countries. Past IEA studies focusing on the use of educational opportunity as a context for understanding international achievement comparisons had produced informative and interesting results suggesting the importance of opportunity-to-learn measures. It was the goal of SMSO to focus efforts towards improving the measurement of these primary concepts. It was believed the work would then enable TIMSS to provide better characterizations of opportunity to learn in relationship to achievement level differences both among and within countries and to explain the curricular context from which these differences at least in part arise.

SMSO was funded through a development grant from the National Science Foundation in conjunction with the National Center for Education Statistics. The project developed and piloted questionnaires for TIMSS related to teachers' conceptions of subject matter, pedagogical beliefs, background, content goals, student opportunities to learn, and classroom instructional practices. These questionnaires were piloted in France, Japan, Norway, Spain, Switzerland, and the United

States. In addition, over 120 classroom observations were completed in six countries related to instructional practices and opportunity to learn which contributed to the development of a model of educational opportunity which undergirds the TIMSS instrumentation.

The work of Geoffrey Howson is especially relevant to this project as he reviewed and analyzed textbooks in the six SMSO countries and in two additional countries: England and the Netherlands. The monograph by Dr. Howson provides an introduction to some of the issues that will be addressed in the larger curriculum analysis completed in approximately 45 countries for the Third International Mathematics and Science Study.

William H. Schmidt
Director of SMSO
National Research Coordinator for TIMSS
United States

Introduction

Textbooks and the Third International Mathematics and Science Study

The work of the International Association for Educational Achievement (IEA) is often associated in the minds of educators only with the attainment tests, a kind of Educational Olympics, which take place from time to time and result in the publication in the press of ranking lists of questionable value and validity. Mathematics educators may also associate the IEA with a particularly critical paper written by Hans Freudenthal following the First International Mathematics Study (Freudenthal, 1975). In fact, however, IEA'S work is concerned with much more than student attainment (see, for example, Travers and Westbury, 1989). Certainly its aims go far beyond producing ordered lists of countries; and comparative curriculum analysis is a major feature of TIMSS, the Third International Mathematics and Science Study. This aspect of the study is being undertaken in a variety of ways: through consideration of the different ages at which particular mathematical topics are introduced, the grades during which they are studied and any years in which particular emphasis is laid upon them; by a similar, but more "in-depth" look at certain key topics (place value and decimals, fractions and proportionality, geometry, linear equations, measurement, and data analysis); and by means of "document analysis." It is in this last component that attention is focused upon textbooks and curriculum guides. Indeed, this particular project in the comparative analysis of texts must be the largest and most ambitious ever undertaken. Texts for fourth-, eighth-, and twelfth-graders (9-, 13-, and 17-year-olds) in over forty countries are being analyzed according to certain major characteristics:

1. Topics covered.[1]

2. Student performance expectations (for example, communicating, using routine procedures, problem-solving).

3. Instructional features (such as narrative prose, use of graphics).

4. Perspectives (for example, historical features, attitudes engendered towards mathematics).

The participating countries had to determine which textbooks would best represent their nation. This often meant a number of books being analyzed at each level, especially in those countries with curricula determined by land or canton. In general, the most widely used textbooks were selected, although this was not invariably the case. For coding purposes, textbooks were divided into *units of analysis* (requiring one to three periods of 45-60 minutes of instructional time), which were in turn subdivided into *blocks*, such as narrative, graphic, sets of questions/exercises, activities/experiments, worked examples. All these textual components were then coded (components were often coded in more than one category).

Clearly, the reliability and subsequent value of such a process depend on the consistency with which the coding was undertaken in the participating countries. Training sessions were held in several locations throughout the world in an attempt to ensure an acceptable degree of consistency.

In addition to this coding of textbooks, countries were asked to complete a document analysis form which allowed them to make more qualitative remarks about the textbooks as well as supplying information on their degree of acceptance, and publication and other details.

It is expected that preliminary findings from this textbook analysis will be published in late 1995.

The project will provide much data about textbooks worldwide. However, it was thought sensible to supplement this with a less ambitious, qualitative study of particular mathematics texts written for eighth-graders. This study would be more subjective and would be carried out by a single person who would not only be able to provide some check on the validity of the findings of the main study, but would also be able to consider aspects of textbooks beyond that study's scope. I was asked to carry out this task, and my findings form the basis for what follows. *It must be stressed, however, that this is a qualitative and subjective report. The views expressed in it are those of the author and do not necessarily reflect those of IEA or of TIMSS.*

The Books Analyzed

The books included in this analysis are taken from countries participating in the Survey of Mathematics and Science Opportunity Project plus texts from the United Kingdom and the Netherlands. Where appropriate the same texts were studied as in the more general analysis described earlier. One result of this is that all the analyses are of textbooks and none of other forms of learning materials. However, although examples can be cited of the use of individualized booklets or cards and of other types of commercially produced classroom materials, it remains the case that in all the countries considered the textbook still remains the main published aid to learning and teaching. Nevertheless, it is somewhat disappointing that, with one exception, the books all followed the same basic pattern (with many surface differences). There was no evidence of the use of such procedures as the use of dialogue, even as a part of the text, or, at this grade, of programmed texts or topic books. It is possible that such publications could be found in certain countries, but I cannot recall seeing any submitted to even the major textbook study and this suggests that, if they exist, they are used only by a minority of students.

The books analyzed are those used for grade 8 pupils (usually 13-year-olds), but those for grades 7 and 9 have been consulted where appropriate in order to see how topics are first introduced or developed, and the amount of recapitulation (review).

Texts Analyzed

England
School Mathematics Project, SMP *Books B 1 and 2*, Cambridge University Press, 1985 (124, 124 pp., medium format)

France
Bonnefand, G. et al., *Pythagore 4e*, Hatier, 1992 (256 pp., large format)

Japan
Iwago, K. et al., *Mathematics for Secondary School 2*, 1993 (219 pp., small format); Seki, S. et al., *Secondary School Mathematics 2*, Dai Nippon Tosho, 1993 (211 pp., small format)

The Netherlands
Bosman, R.M. et al., *Moderne Wiskunde 2lm*, Wolters-Noordhoff, 1990 (260 pp., medium format)

Norway
Westbye, O., *min matematikk 7*, NKS-Forlaget, 1988 (357 pp., medium format)

Spain
Equipo Signo, *Azimut Matemáticas 8*, Anaya, 1992 (286 pp., large format)

Switzerland
Boss, R. et al., *Mathematik 7*, Staatlicher Lehrmittelverlag Bern, 1985 (128 pp., small format)

U.S.A.
Bolster, L.C., et al., *Exploring Mathematics 8*, Scott Foresman, 1991 (651 pp., large format)

Certain key points relating to these texts must be clearly identified at this point. First, it will be seen that the texts from Norway and Switzerland are for grade 7 rather than grade 8. This reflects the fact that children enter primary schools in Norway and the canton of Berne one year later than in most other countries (see the discussion of arithmetic in chapter 3). However, because of the "catching up" which occurs it seemed more appropriate to use the grade 7 books for 13-year-olds than those for grade 8. In contrast, the English textbook is one for year 9 in that system, for children in England begin formal primary education at age 5. Secondly, the Swiss example illustrates that there can be very significant differences of structure and curricula within a single country. Switzerland has 26 autonomous cantons and Spain 17 autonomous communities. So, for example, children in the Ticino (Italian-speaking Switzerland) begin primary school a year earlier than do children in Berne, and the curriculum in Catalonia exhibits differences from those elsewhere in Spain. It must be realized, therefore, that when, for the sake of brevity, we refer to the Swiss text, this is shorthand for the text from the canton of Berne.

Another complication arises because the texts studied are not always intended for the same groups of students (see chapter 2). In England, the Netherlands, and Switzerland, students are divided into different groups according to attainment and perceived ability (either nationally or within individual schools). The texts selected to be analyzed from these countries are those used by the median pupil. Even so, the target users of the English texts differ from those of the texts from the Netherlands and Switzerland. The problems of the differentiation of students will be considered more fully in chapter 2, but this key difference must always be kept in mind.

A recurring problem in any comparative study is that changes are always taking place in educational systems and their national curricula. Thus it should be noted that planned changes are to be implemented in the school structure in Berne, and in the national curricula in that canton, in England, the Netherlands, and Spain, and that these changes are not reflected in the books studied.

A final *caveat* must be to emphasize that although in later sections we shall refer to, say, *the* French text, this is again a shorthand for "the French text studied." A single text cannot be taken as representative of all of those to be found in a particular country. Other texts will have different strengths and weaknesses. The texts studied provide indications—they contain messages, but they are not determinants of national characteristics or necessarily of classroom practice.

Note

[1] The curriculum framework used in this study is described in the first of the TIMSS monograph series, *Curriculum Frameworks for Mathematics and Science*, Pacific Educational Press, 1993.

Chapter 1

The Textbook: Its History and Its Role

This chapter provides a brief overview of textbooks, their place in mathematics education and how they have evolved, and a short survey of research which has been carried out into texts and the focus of different investigations. The chapter will, therefore, provide us with a variety of questions that can be asked of a mathematical text—not all of which will be considered in this particular study.

Perspectives on Textbooks

The recently published Japanese series, *Chugaku Sugakaku* (*Mathematics for Secondary School,* 1993), begins every chapter with a "chatty" problem illustrated in cartoon style. The chapter on similarity of figures, for example, starts with the discussion of the practical problem: "How can we find the width of a river without crossing to the other side?" The girl shown in the book holds a drawing which will help lead to the answer, based on the use of similar triangles. The same problem and essentially the same diagram may be found in A.C. Clairaut's revolutionary *Elements of Geometry,* first published over 250 years earlier in 1741. Indeed, the relevant page of Clairaut is reproduced in Ogura's *History of Mathematics Education* (Tokyo, 1932), a work based on a study of mathematics textbooks through the ages.

This example gives rise to much of interest. At a first glance we see the way in which much mathematics, including specific examples, is handed down over the centuries through the medium of the textbook. The reference to Ogura's *History* also demonstrates the key role which textbooks play in illustrating contemporary thoughts about, and aims within, mathematics education. They have long been used as a source for research into how, and what, mathematics was learned; the TIMSS study is part of a long tradition.

Yet the very choice of Clairaut's work brings other, less apparent issues to our attention. Clairaut's book represented a novel approach to the teaching of geometry, and its interest for present day readers lies not so much in its mathematical content but in the philosophical and pedagogical considerations which underpin its presentation of the mathematics. Here is an extract from Clairaut's preface to his book:

> Although Geometry be in itself abstract, it must be admitted that the difficulties felt by [beginners] most frequently arise from the manner in which it is taught in ordinary elementary works. They generally begin with a great number of definitions, postulates, axioms and preliminary principles, which seem to promise nothing but dryness to the reader.... It commonly happens that beginners become wearied and discouraged before they get any distinct idea of what it is desired to teach them. It is true that to avoid ... dryness ... some authors have stated after every important proposition the practical use to which it can be applied, but while they thus prove the utility of Geometry they do not facilitate its study; for as every proposition comes before its application the mind does not return to concrete objects till after it has undergone the fatigue of conceiving abstract ideas. [With these considerations in mind] I have resolved to go back to that which may have given birth to Geometry ... I intend ... to give beginners means of discovering the principles on which simple measurement of lands and of accessible and inaccessible distances, etc., may be made to depend. Thence I will proceed to other researches of a nature so analogous to the first, that the curiosity natural to all men must lead them so far; and by afterwards gratifying that curiosity by some useful applications, I will proceed to discuss all the most interesting subjects of Elementary Geometry. I hope ... that this method [will not only] encourage those

who might be repelled by the dryness of geometrical truths when
stripped of their application ... but ... that it may accustom the mind
to seek and to discover.[1]

Clairaut's preface may well come as a surprise to those who believe that serious thought on the pedagogy of mathematics is of com-
paratively recent origin. Matters such as the pedagogical ordering of
material and the needs to provide motivation, present mathematics in
context, and develop natural curiosity in such a way that it is chan-
nelled towards mathematical discovery are all explicitly recognized.[2]
Moreover, Clairaut's interest was neither unique nor unprecedented.
For example, Robert Recorde, who in the sixteenth century wrote the
first series of mathematics texts in English, specifically mentioned
the limitations of learning by rote; that understanding is vital for those
wishing to become "cunning indeed in the art," but that on occasions
full understanding must follow the acquisition of technique; the desirability of using language for terms which carries meaning for students; and the need to distinguish between the abstract nature of the
geometer's system and the needs and intuitions of the ordinary person.[3]

Yet it must be remembered that Clairaut's and Recorde's books
were not written for use in an institutionalized school system in which
students were working towards examination qualifications. The relation of the text with the reader, then, differed from that of a present
day school text. There are no sets of exercises, the works are not presented in terms of a series of readily identifiable "lessons," and, most
importantly, the presence of a mediating teacher is not assumed.[4] It is
important, then, to remember that the nature of texts evolves together
with the social and other educational contexts within which they are
intended to be used and that the books which we shall be studying
assume particular classroom and social milieux.

So as to establish a better relationship with his readers, Recorde,
in most of his texts, presented the mathematics in the form of a dialogue between teacher and pupil, a type of presentation used from
Plato onwards. It adds another dimension to the book than mere exposition, for the reader can associate with the pupil's doubts, misun-

Little has changed in the presentation or solution of a geometry problem. A.C. Clairaut's eighteenth-century approach is cited in Ogura's History of Mathematics *from the 1930s and again in a contemporary Japanese textbook.*

derstandings, and queries. The average text is likely to present mathematics in a monolithic way: "this is how it is done, now go and do it for yourself." No individuality is acknowledged or allowed in the way in which mathematics is approached. The dialogue form, particularly in an extended version, allows something to be done to counter this: varying points of view can be stated and readers can be permitted to see that a problem can be viewed and approached from different standpoints. This technique was used in the highly influential book by Lakatos, *Proofs and Refutations* (1976). In that work the various discussants represent different philosophical standpoints. Somewhat earlier, in the 1960s, Lucienne Félix attempted something similar in a mathematics text. She made use of three characters, each representing different biases in their approach to mathematics: Dessi, who draws and makes deductions, Mati, who does the mathematical thinking, and Logi, who reduces all to abstract ideas. Thus we see plainly acknowledged what all research mathematicians know: not all professional mathematicians share the same strengths or approach a problem in the same way—something which is doubtless also true for students but which the standard textbook does not take into account.

At the same time that Mme Félix was attempting to demonstrate an approach to mathematics which acknowledged individual personality differences, there was also considerable interest in an approach which took an opposite view. This, by eliminating the influence of the classroom teacher, sought to guide all readers through a rigidly imposed program. Early this century the U.S. educator, Thorndike, wrote that personal instruction for all would be guaranteed if only one could produce a book arranged so that page two was invisible until the directions outlined on page one were carried out. This idea was taken up with enthusiasm in the 1950s by the psychologist, Skinner, who led what became known as the "programmed learning movement." Various projects (see, for example, Howson et al., 1981, for details) produced classroom texts and materials seeking to exemplify this approach which was given further support with the advent of the computer which effectively denied students the opportunity to see page two until they had demonstrated their ability to answer correctly questions set on page one. The simplistic nature of this "pure" behaviourist approach was quickly realized, and it is no longer a major educational force. On the other hand, the complications of the approach pioneered by Mme Félix have deterred further experiments in that direction.

The textbook, then, has not always had a stable form. Various attempts have been made to introduce radically new models and even the model most favoured nowadays is still gradually evolving.

In a famous talk given at the Second International Congress on Mathematics Education, René Thom (1973) argued that "all mathematical pedagogy, even if scarcely coherent, rests on a philosophy of mathematics." This statement applies very strongly to texts. One of the aims of this monograph is to consider the beliefs, approaches, aims, and expectations to be found in a sample of textbooks drawn from a variety of countries. In particular, I shall consider apparent assumptions concerning the manner in which teachers will use the materials in the classroom. It is not claimed that these investigations will in any way define national characteristics, for the choice of materials may well not be representative. It is also clear that although the textbook takes us one step nearer classroom reality than does, say, a national curriculum, it cannot be taken as a determinant of what happens within classrooms. Although the great majority of teachers, particularly those in high schools, would seem to use textbooks, the way in which they do this differs greatly (see, for example, Goffree, 1985). (One of the aims of TIMSS is to obtain data on the use of textbooks, and their influence on teachers and on what happens in the classroom.) In addition to introducing pedagogical variants teachers will also omit topics according to what they perceive as the particular needs and capabilities of their students, their views of what should comprise school mathematics, and, often, their own mathematical deficiencies (see, for example, Travers and Westbury, op. cit.). Moreover, it must be accepted that the "beliefs" illustrated in a textbook do not necessarily reflect the author's true beliefs concerning pedagogy— any more, in fact, than a particular lesson will necessarily reflect a teacher's underlying philosophy on pedagogy. A textbook is written with many constraints in mind: for example, the educational system for which it is intended, the degree of professionalism of the teaching force, the financial resources available to schools and for in-service training, and, in an open market, publishers who seek commercial success. All such constraints rule out some possibilities and ensure that any textbook will represent a compromise of some form. Nevertheless, textual analysis will cast light on the actual position as it is perceived by textbook authors, reveal something about current practice in many countries, and draw attention to current thinking about the place of written materials in the classroom and to the essential characteristics of these. Constraints on space will, of course, limit the depth of the analyses, yet even so we hope that this monograph will serve to promote further research into textual materials and their use in the classroom.

Research on Textbooks

It is a remarkable feature of the NCTM's *Handbook of Research on Mathematics Teaching and Learning* (Grouws, 1992) that there is no entry in the subject index under "textbooks." There is a single entry for "textbook analyses" and that is that. Of course, there are references to texts scattered throughout the book, but these are few and far between, and clearly were not thought sufficiently important to merit an entry in the index. A chapter is devoted to "Technology" and this contains an extremely long and valuable list of references. But despite the obvious powers of the new technology it must be accepted that its role in the vast majority of the world's classrooms pales into insignificance when compared with that of textbooks and other written materials.

What are the reasons for this striking omission? Reference to *Zentralblatt für Didaktik der Mathematik, Journal for Research in Mathematics Education,* and *Educational Studies in Mathematics* suggests that one reason might be the paucity of research papers on this aspect of mathematics education. Certainly, there are great problems attached to *a posteriori* research on texts, that is, work undertaken to consider in what ways the text has been used in classrooms, how it has contributed to the learning process, and what obstacles to learning it has presented. More work has been undertaken on textual analysis away from the classroom. Without wishing to give the impression of providing a summary of all such work, one can draw attention to several examples of interest. Reference has already been made to Ogura's pioneering history of mathematics education which was based almost entirely on the analysis of texts. More recently there has been much work in this field by an international group with particularly strong French and German representation (see, for example, Jahnke, 1994). Such work might be dismissed as being academic researches into history. However, educational problems have a habit of reappearing in a new guise and an understanding of the problems of assimilation which arose in the past may well throw light on current issues. There was great opposition in the early nineteenth century, for example, to the introduction of algebraic (coordinate) methods into geometry teaching. Students could get answers by "mechanical" means without understanding what was happening geometrically. Was this acceptable and consonant with wider educational aims? What of the "old" geometry was still essential to a well-balanced education? Similar questions can now be posed about arithmetic and the calculator.

Textbook analysis has also proved a useful weapon for drawing attention to the disparities in aims and expectations which exist between educational systems and for promoting political action (see, for example, Wirszup, 1981, Stevenson et al., 1986). What is taught and what is learned are, of course, closely connected and the resulting emphasis in comparative studies on attainment and opportunities to learn is a natural one.

Two aspects of texts, language and readability, have exercised the minds of researchers drawn from all subject areas. Language affects mathematics teaching in many ways: classroom discussion, complexity of language, choice of registers, social and ethnic problems, and bilingualism, among others (see, for example, Pimm, 1987; Secada, 1992). Many of these aspects arise in connection with texts. Readability and the use of a vocabulary which does not further disadvantage minorities (or even majorities!) spring immediately to mind. The former has been the subject of much research, but tests devised for assessing normal prose do not always possess much validity when applied to mathematics texts. In these, multisyllabic technical terms are common and technical prose tends to be precise and lacking in redundancy. One book which looks at the special problems of language in mathematics texts is Shuard and Rothery (1983). This aspect of texts is often ignored in comparative studies. Judging the "readability" of a text written in one's native tongue is far from easy. It would be foolhardy, however, to attempt judgements on books written in a language in which one lacks knowledge of students' normal linguistic development. In this study, then, we shall only comment on limited aspects of language, for example, on the extra precision in the use of terms to be found in the French text.

Deep questions arise concerning what can be transmitted by text, the relationship between knowledge and its textual representation, and the extent to which interpretations will vary (see, for example, Otte, 1986). Special considerations apply within mathematics since we learn the subject not simply by reading a text, but through activities largely suggested, either implicitly or explicitly, by the text. A mathematics text cannot be judged, then, simply by the exposition it presents: the range and richness of the activities to which it gives rise must also be considered. The number of exercises contained in a text is not by itself a very significant variable: their range and potential for promoting learning, understanding, retention, discovery, and motivation are. (An interesting reference in this area is *Text, Wissen, Tätigkeit: Das Schulbuch in Mathematikerunterricht,* [Keitel, Otte, Seeger, 1980]. Unfortunately, it has not appeared in English translation.)

This list of *a priori* research types could be much extended. Here we give only three further examples. My students have always found van Dormolen (1986) immediately useful in focussing their attention upon particular aspects of texts: what one might refer to as their mathematical and pedagogical clarity. (Reference is made to this paper, and a brief description given, below.) Keitel (1987) presents an interesting *a priori* criticism of a set of textual materials (because it was largely based on general, rather than specific observations) which fitted very well with later findings in classrooms. This is a paper which illustrates the value of knowledge of past experiences and experiments, and of students' extra-mathematical behaviour and motivation: powerful influences which may well dominate those which textbook authors seek to assert. The question of gender bias in texts gave rise to considerable research in the 1970s and this was soon widened to the consideration of other racial and ethnic biases and to the "social messages" carried by texts (see, for example, Dowling, 1991).

More general, *a posteriori* evaluation of texts was fairly frequently undertaken in the 1960s and '70s, as part of project evaluations, but less has been done in recent years as money has become hard to obtain for what is of necessity very expensive work (and which often simply reveals flaws that have become apparent to all involved within the classroom). Descriptions of various evaluations can be found in Howson et al. (1981). Regrettably, many findings of the effect on teachers, their perceptions of their role, and the sudden transplantation of "individualized" materials into their classrooms (see, for example, Morgan, 1977) appear to have gone unnoticed or unheeded. Much that was contained in such work was of wider application and concern than the particular series of texts with which the investigations were concerned. A recent report by Bell et al. (1993) approaches the subject from a different point of view and considers the student's ability to appreciate the nature of a mathematical text. Here, the work is not directed at a particular text but rather the research explores possible interactions (not all one way) between student and text. A more conventional form of research, even though infrequently attempted, is described in Gravemeijer (1994). This is a summary of the findings of a Netherlands project which sought to find how successful different textbooks had been in implementing planned reforms and the resulting effects on students and teachers.

What is disturbing is that would-be textbook authors still have few significant research papers or studies to which they can turn for guidance on how they might best present materials to improve classroom practices and students' "deeper" learning and attitudes towards mathematics. How, for example, does one produce materials that themselves play a part in "freeing teachers from the tyranny of texts" (to borrow a title from Ben-Peretz, 1990) while realizing the need to free pupils from the tyranny of ill-prepared teachers who believe they can do without the aid of texts? What, for example, can be said about the degree of practice required by students to obtain desired technical proficiency? Certainly, texts would seem to vary considerably in the assumptions they make about this (see chapter 3). It is my hope that this monograph will promote a greater interest in research work in this field, for it is intended to foster interest in the area in addition to presenting particular findings.

The Role of the Textbook

The textbook is called upon to play many different roles. It provides a source of problems and exercises; it may also act as a reference book setting out what van Dormolen, op. cit., refers to as the "kernels" of instruction—theorems, rules, definitions, procedures, notations, and conventions which "have to be learned as knowledge." Some texts also devote considerable space to "explanations"—not themselves kernels—which prepare the students for the kernels. In so doing, the texts act as a teacher in themselves and, it may be argued, affect the classroom teacher's authority and professionalism. We have already referred to occasions on which it has been attempted to go so far as to supply "teacher-free" texts.

Indeed, various approaches can be discerned in the books analyzed. One stands apart from all the others: that from the canton of Berne in Switzerland, intended for the use of students in the lower half of the ability range. This is not a conventional "text," but a collection of 387 "questions" (the reason for the quotation marks will be made clear later) arranged into nine chapters, each subdivided into sections. The book contains no narrative or reviews, and only the occasional kernel. (It does include two pages of definitions and explanations of notation at the end.) It reflects an interesting alternative to the other textbooks studied. Using this text, the teacher has an added degree of autonomy and responsibility. He or she must decide on how best to introduce a topic, although considerable help is provided by a teachers' guide. The teacher is responsible for identifying key kernels—definitions, procedures, results, and so on—and ensuring that students make notes of these, but the opportunity is now presented of negotiating definitions or procedures with the class, without the constraint of having an "official" version there for all to see in the textbook. There is some freedom in determining the sequencing of topics. Moreover, not all the "questions" are predetermined problems. Some simply provide data on a particular subject, for example, the different types of calls dealt with by the Berne fire service in a given year. The teacher is then free to develop questions around these data—be they on graphical representation, percentages, probabilities, or whatever. Even better, students can be encouraged to pose and answer their own questions on the topic. (Similar data-banks are to be found in some of the other texts.)

Such a text, then, offers teachers considerable autonomy, but at the expense of making great demands on their professionalism and their willingness to commit more time to the preparation of lessons (at least, in the teachers' initial years of teaching). In the hands of a good teacher, students may be offered a richer and more varied diet. However, students obtain no experience in reading a mathematical text or in appreciating its nature. Practical problems may arise when students are absent for a few days and cannot then be asked to read about the topic on their own, but this and other problems can be alleviated through the complementary use of more conventional, nonofficial textbooks and/or other textual materials.

It is perhaps worthy of note, that the texts used in Berne by the high-ability students are on algebra and geometry. These contrast with all the other texts considered in this study which contain all the mathematics intended to be studied in a particular grade. There is a conflict between greater teacher autonomy, the ability to decide how and when to allocate time to the different branches of mathematics, and a wish to present mathematics as a unified subject in which the interdependencies of the various components of mathematics and the way in which they are sequenced and linked in the text, frequently dictate a particular order of treatment to the teacher. The Swiss text is also of interest to the extent to which it is an "official" document essentially defining the curriculum not in words which have to be interpreted, but by means of exemplary tasks. It thus supplements an official but brief description of content to be studied in year 7 which distinguishes clearly between what is seen as compulsory core content and what is optional. (In countries with a centralized examination system, a similar role is played by the test items which are set.)

Perhaps the nearest to the Swiss text in its emphasis on examples and activities and its almost complete lack of attention paid to kernels is the School Mathematics Project series.[5] Yet, such is the multi-dimensional nature of mathematics texts, it can be interpreted as standing perhaps furthest from the Swiss series in the demands it makes on the teacher.

The SMP 11-16 series, which is immensely popular in England, is in two parts. The first two years, 11-13, consist of short booklets supporting independent learning by the students. In the final three years, 13-16, the course is presented in textbook form, but at different levels suited to students' attainment (see chapter 2). However, the emphasis is still on the presentation of topics through tasks: sequences of simple problems which have been carefully chosen so as to lead students gradually through the topic and have been constructed bearing in mind recent research findings on students' misconceptions and common errors. In theory, these texts offer the same opportunities for discussion of kernels as do the Swiss, provided the class or a group of pupils come together to negotiate these after working through the relevant sections (see Bell et al., 1993 for suggestions on how this may be done). Yet the fact that the texts are readily accessible to pupils can lead teachers to consider the books to be self-sufficient (an impression unfortunately reinforced by the teachers' guides, which are little more than answer books). Students will then be given insufficient help in structuring their experiences and determining what constitutes worthwhile or essential knowledge. The lack of an index—or better still, a mini-dictionary/glossary as in the French and U.S. texts—again conceals the need to record and make ready reference to acquired mathematical knowledge.[6]

The Japanese texts are in marked contrast to the Swiss and English ones. I was able, thanks to the assistance provided by Professor T. Nakahara, to study two series from Japan. A third series was considered in the main study. The similarities between the three series are staggering to one brought up on a rich diversity of texts. All grade

8 books are of approximately the same length, and each contains eight chapters and has roughly the same chapter titles. There are detectable differences in pedagogy and depth of treatment, but in general the books reflect that social homogeneity which tends to characterize Japanese life. Considerable structure is provided for teacher and pupils within an expected scheme of presentation. It is normally easy to discern what is intended to be a "lesson's work." Yet the pupils' books are supported by well documented teachers' guides which offer suggestions for alternative approaches (and it must be emphasized that the classes I saw on a recent visit to Japan were not as "textbook"-bound as many I have encountered elsewhere, even though the range of teaching techniques on display was very limited). Certainly, a new teacher in Japan is afforded a very supportive framework from which he or she may later diverge. The books from the Netherlands, Norway, and Spain share much in common with the Japanese texts so far as their relation to the teachers was concerned, although, as will be explained below, they differ significantly in many other respects. The French text is distinguished by its particular separation of kernels. Reference has already been made to its excellent "mini-dictionary," but other types of kernels are also identified clearly by means of the "box of tools" and the "box of methods" to be found in each chapter. Other features of the French text reflect its authors' response to the problems of differentiation of students within a comprehensive school system and will be discussed later.

The problem of the U.S. text is readily identified given the number of its pages and the fact that it appears in a large format. Those coding the text for the main TIMSS study found that it contained over three hundred units—each requiring one to three periods of class time! There is material here for three grades' work. Some is review of material covered in previous years, much is new; some reflects all that is novel in the NCTM *Standards* (1989), some appears very traditional.[7] Teachers are left, with the aid of a voluminous teachers' guide, to devise a one-year course appropriate for students of very differing abilities and achievements. They do not face the same problems of preparation as the Swiss, but the problems of selection of material are great (although advice is to be found in the accompanying guide). Moreover, there will be a problem of reorientation and preparation if teachers are to forsake well-worn traditional paths for those advocated in the *Standards*. The result is that although a study of the Japanese books provides a reasonable idea of what will be taught in their classrooms, just about anything might happen in a U.S. classroom using this particular series of texts. For the U.S. text, although not advertising this fact, is not a *course*, but rather a *resource*. As indicated earlier, it is written very much with the *Standards* in mind. This serves to remind us that textbooks can also have a role within a system rather than merely within individual classrooms. In some circumstances a textbook series can attempt to establish new content or pedagogical norms. In particular, it may be seen as attempting to meet one or more of the following goals:

1. Fleshing out a centrally prescribed curriculum.

2. Attempting to update pedagogy within a centrally prescribed curriculum.

3. Responding to new, non-statutory proposals on pedagogy, for example, NCTM's *Standards* or the "Cockcroft" *Report* (DES, 1982).

4. Helping to define a new curriculum.

The exact aims which a textbook can have are, of course, determined by the nature of the country's educational system. Of necessity, Japan's texts can only aim at goals (1) and (2). All of its series attempt to put flesh on the new, skeletal national curriculum, but in addition they can seek, as one co-author expressed it, "to increase pupils' motivation, to proceed from the concrete to the abstract [that is, to make greater use of contextualized examples and problems] and to set normally one kernel a lesson." The French text is a revision of an already popular text (1988) and contains many innovations directed at (2), for example, a greater use of technological aids. As we have seen, the U.S. text aims primarily at (3) but also at (4), whereas the SMP text (written in non-centrally directed times) reversed these priorities. A planned, total rewrite of the SMP 11-16 materials must now seek to satisfy (1) and (2), whilst still hoping to achieve some success with (4).

In the sections which follow we shall look in some detail at certain aspects of texts, namely, the actual package presented to teachers and its provenance, and in the chapters which follow we shall look at the pedagogical and philosophical assumptions implicit in texts, their pedagogical structure, their mathematical content—including acceptance of technology, and the extent to which they link with the school curriculum as a whole, with society and culture.

The Production and Selection of Textual Materials

The Provenance of Texts

The manner in which texts are provided varies significantly from country to country as does the freedom of teachers to select texts of their own choice.

In some countries, particularly those in eastern Europe, there has in the past only been a single, state-sponsored text available to teachers. These were often produced by teams established by the Ministry of Education. However, with one exception all the texts included in this particular study were produced by commercial publishers and were in direct competition with other series of texts. The exception is the Swiss text which is published by the canton of Berne, but which, nevertheless, is not the only text available to teachers.

What is very noticeable is the way in which so many of the texts are written by teams of authors. In the past two decades, there has been a significant move away from the individual authorship of texts, possibly as a result of the many projects of the 1960s and '70s which made great use of writing teams.[8]

Nevertheless, there are still very marked differences in the composition of the teams of authors. Thus, for example, twenty authors contributed to the Japanese series, *Mathematics for Secondary School:* 15 mathematics educators (some involved in teacher education), 4 serving teachers and 1 "other." The U.S. text lists 25 "authors" (8 co-ordinators/advisers/specialist teachers, 9 educators—including mathematics educators, 6 mathematicians, 1 assistant principal, and 1 other), a "contributing author" (publisher), 6 consultants (university specialists) and 14 "critic readers" (schoolteachers). SMP used a large number of contributors, almost all serving teachers, to prepare early drafts that were then put into a final form by a team of 5 full-time writers who had previously been schoolteachers. Other textbooks studied drew on the experiences and work of fewer authors, but none was written by an individual. The Norwegian book was unique in being an adaptation of a text originally written for use in another country (Sweden).

It would be tempting to make inferences based upon the compositions of the various teams. Certainly it would be true to say that the strong bias of SMP in favour of teachers resulted in a text which had considerable appeal to pupils and reduced the amount of "hassle" in the classroom. One might also attribute the lack of emphasis on kernels to this bias, but this is not usually a feature of teacher-authored texts. On the other hand, the SMP teachers appear to have made a greater effort to use research results than have other sets of authors, many of which listed mathematics educators amongst their members.

Indeed, at a first glance, it is not the differences in approach between the various texts which appear particularly significant, but rather their uniformity—their more or less common view concerning what school mathematics is about and how it should be learned.

Another significant feature of the projects of the '60s and '70s was the use of draft or trial texts. I believe that of the books reviewed here only the SMP text was tested in the classroom. This, however, would not seem of great relevance. The texts, in general, follow well-worn pedagogical paths (with the exception of the U.S. text which makes no great commitment to any new one) and none introduces any markedly new mathematical content. We are not here considering the likes of the books produced by Papy, Dienes, or the School Mathematics Study Group; any innovations that have been incorporated into the texts reflect extension by analytic continuation rather than catastrophic changes.

The question of the use of classroom testing opens up much larger considerations relating to the production of texts. The reforms of the

1960s were not only far-reaching so far as goals were concerned, but they took place in what now appears to have been a very stable educational and technological context. Of course, there was the very early Suppes Project on the use of computer assisted instruction in mathematics and, indeed, IBM provided eight or so SMP schools with prototype (but very simple!) stand-on-a-desk computers in the late 1960s. It must be remembered, too, that Papert excited those at the 1972 ICME with talk of what could be done with "turtle geometry" and how it would/could affect the teaching of school mathematics. But such experiments were seen as very avant garde: mainframe computers were not for schools and IBM refused to make their extremely successful prototype commercially available. Now appropriate hardware is more readily available in many countries, the development of computer graphics has revolutionized the computer's possible contribution to mathematics teaching, and, most significantly, technological advances occur annually. In the '60s and '70s a textbook could be written with an expected life of ten years (in which case it made great sense to polish it through the use of classroom-tested drafts), but today one knows that it will be technologically out of date by the time it appears. Nowadays, the vital question to be answered is not so much what the textbook should do about technological progress, but whether the textbook's role should now be played through technology. Are the textbook's days numbered now that it has become possible to assemble on a readily accessible disk many approaches to teaching a topic and collections of problems coded according to content, difficulty, open-endedness, and other characteristics?

The underlying problem is not one of technology but of money. Texts are relatively cheap ways of packaging mathematical instruction. Moreover, in some countries their cost is borne directly by parents and not indirectly by taxes via the national educational system. In both cases, economic considerations may well result in great pressures to prolong the lifespan of texts well beyond their "best by" date. Whether or not some published alternatives to texts with an appeal for the mass market can be prepared poses an interesting challenge to curriculum developers. However, it is unlikely that any alternative which does not ask the teacher to devote more time to preparation and also to accept greater responsibility, will prove an economical rival.

Teachers' Choice and Supplementary Materials

The degree of freedom teachers have in choosing a text varies from country to country. At one extreme is the liberty for a school to choose for itself from competing series with no restrictions whatsoever placed upon it. At another, texts must be approved at either a national or at some intermediate level above that of the school and schools may only select from a given list. In some parts of Japan, for example, it is the custom for the teachers from a particular area to come together to select the one series which all of them will use.

What is surprising is the lack of research into what influences teachers when selecting texts. No doubt that research has been carried out by publishers within large and lucrative systems such as the U.S., but I cannot recall any papers on this important topic in the educational press.

What do teachers look for? Challenges, or the opposite? Novelty, or re-packaged routine? What degree of autonomy is sought? To what extent is the packaging influential—full colour, typographical excellence, cartoons and photographs? To what degree are support materials and/or arrangements taken into consideration?

Clearly, teachers will differ in their priorities and preferences. Nevertheless, it would be interesting and valuable, for in-service and other purposes, to know more about these.

As already indicated, there are accompanying teachers' guides to most, if not all, of the books reviewed. Many also offer supplementary work or activity books for students. Some go further and offer stencils or copying masters, overhead transparencies, apparatus and, in a very few cases, software.

The most common aid is the teachers' guide. As already indicated, these vary from what are little more than collections of answers, to guides which reproduce a reduced form of the pupils' text (such as those used in France, Japan, and the U.S.) together with notes on the aims of particular passages of text and on the problems set.

Advice may also be given on where stress should be laid, on alternative presentations, and/or on appropriate approaches to cope with the problem of differentiation of pupils. Again, research into the design of teachers' guides and their actual use by teachers could prove profitable. (Light should be thrown on this matter by the analysis of the questionnaires which teachers will be completing as part of the TIMSS study.)

What a textbook does not reveal, nor unfortunately the documents submitted to TIMSS, is to what extent the materials are supported by an after-sales service. It has, for example, been a feature of SMP work in the U.K. that not only has in-service training been provided by the project and supplementary materials been produced to meet obvious gaps identified by teachers (see note 6), but help has been given to neighbouring schools which have come together to form "user groups," and outstanding teachers have been recruited to spend three or four years as "development officers" who would, as part of their work, answer requests for help and advice from individual schools. This has only been possible because of the charitable nature of the SMP Trust and the fact that royalties received are ploughed back into the trust's work and not distributed in their entirety amongst authors.

It is important, then, when considering texts, their effectiveness and attractiveness, to take into account not only the books themselves but also the support which the teacher using them can expect to enjoy.

The Design and Visual Appeal of Texts

Whether or not they influence the choice of teachers, the design and visual appeal of texts are clearly of considerable importance to authors and publishers.

Only two of the books studied were in full colour, those from France and the U.S., although the Japanese series had additional full-colour endpapers (supplementary pages between the binding and the text). All the remaining texts had full colour covers but used only one additional colour to enliven the text. (Again, Japan differed by varying the additional colour as one proceeded through the text.) Certainly, the use of full colour adds greatly to the visual attractiveness of the U.S. text, which contains many striking photographs. The French text uses full colour more sparingly. Neither uses colour to significant mathematical ends as did Papy in his 1960s' series *Mathématiques modernes*, or, to go back even further in time, Oliver Byrne in his *Euclid in Colour* (1847). It helps in the U.S. examples of pie charts (circle graphs), but rarely elsewhere. (The equivalent French "camemberts" each have only two pieces and so benefit little mathematically from the use of various colours.) The French book suddenly erupts into visual life in the final chapter when examples of translations and rotations in art and architecture are reproduced.

Most books make good use of typography and the use of bold type or colours to denote kernels. The French book, on the other hand, strikes this reader as badly designed with a multiplicity of type faces and messy page layouts—but that reaction may be too subjective! It would be interesting to ascertain the reponses of students to such issues. Does the appeal of full colour soon wear off—if it adds nothing mathematically? Does good typography exert an appeal by itself?

As indicated, the U.S. texts make much use of photographs. It may not help one overmuch to be shown what a lobster looks like as one works out the mean number of lobsters sold per day by "Sherri's Seafood Shop," but no doubt this could be justified on the grounds of "cross-curricular work." Certainly, it lifts the page visually.

A number of texts, including those from England, France, and the Netherlands, make use of cartoons, and the Netherlands text even introduces a poem in an attempt to stimulate interest. Again, it is difficult to judge how the majority of students will react to such initiatives. The cartoons do not always add much educationally, but they do "lighten" the atmosphere. It would be valuable to know whether or not they are achieving their aims of making mathematics learning more attractive and accessible.

Notes

[1] A.C. Clairaut, *Elements of Geometry* (1881).

[2] Consideration of Clairaut's pedagogical aims and attainments are to be found in, for example, Glaeser (1984).

[3] See, for example, Howson (1982).

[4] Recorde makes it clear that his *Ground of Artes* is written for "suche as shall lack instructers." He also realizes that he will have two types of readers: those who study "principalli for lerning" and those who want to use the arithmetic and do not have the time to work for "exacter knowledge."

[5] The School Mathematics Project was one of the many projects established world-wide in the 1960s. However, it differed from most in not being supported from public (state) funds. It is a private charitable trust and the financial success of its materials has enabled it to remain in existence and to carry out a continuous process of revision. It is distinguished by the extent to which it depends upon the input of practising teachers, and in addition to the production of materials it has also been responsible for many innovations in assessment and the in-service education of teachers. Howson (1987) is a collection of essays describing the first twenty-five years of SMP's work.

[6] The deficiencies in the materials have been recognized by the SMP and, for example, the revised booklets and books which have been issued to ensure that the course meets the requirements of the new English national curriculum in mathematics are now accompanied by weightier teachers' guides. In addition, attempts have been made to increase the range of teaching techniques used in SMP classrooms through the publication of guides such as *Using Software, Using Investigations,* and *Using Groupwork.* A revised version of the course is now being prepared but, because of the way this is developed and tested in the classroom in schools, it will not appear before the end of the decade. Readers who may marvel at the rainbow of different texts currently provided for students of different levels of attainment and ability (see chapter 3), may be interested to learn that it is expected

that the new series will lay less stress on such differentiation.

[7] The *Standards*, produced by the National Council of Teachers of Mathematics, reflects an attempt by a community of teachers and mathematics educators to produce goals for the school curriculum. This was essentially a self-regulatory exercise in a country which does not have a national curriculum imposed from on high. Possibly as a result of this, the advice given on content is less prescriptive than usual and more emphasis is paid to process goals.

[8] When team writing first became popular in the 1960s, its merits as against single-authorship were often debated. It was frequently the case that the chapters of "team" books exhibited markedly different approaches and even philosophies. This was counterbalanced by the richness of ideas and the breadth of experience and examples which a team could bring to the task. Judging from the books studied, nowadays group-written books display a far greater degree of homogeneity. It is not possible to tell that chapters have been written by different authors. This change may spring from greater experience of team writing or an acceptance of the need for more rigorous editorship. Nevertheless, it is now hard to envisage a major main-school textbook series being written by a single author.

Chapter 2

The Pedagogy and Philosophy of Mathematics

Perhaps the most important feature of a text is the view of mathematics which it presents. Does mathematics consist of an apparently interminable list of facts and techniques to be learned, or of structures and knowledge to be constructed? The balance of these two viewpoints, the variety of activities encouraged, and the support for independent learning are all important characteristics of a text. What picture does it paint of the way in which mathematics arises: was it handed down on tablets of stone or did it, and does it still, reflect human responses to societal and intellectual challenges? It is difficult to deal with such questions away from specific examples and we shall provide some of these in following sections.

Here, it suffices to admit to a degree of disappointment. There is a great similarity in the way that mathematics is presented in the texts considered. A standard pattern appears to be the presentation of mathematics by chapters, or more basic units, using this structure:

1. Introductory activities or examples.

2. Exploration in some detail of a generic example.

3. Presentation of kernels—definitions, procedures, etc.

4. Consolidation through abstract and contextualized exercises and problems.

Such a pattern has, of course, evolved over the centuries and is extremely economical: it provides both teachers and students with a readily discernible structure (itself no mean aim). Less advantageously, it also results in a homogeneous, monolithic presentation of mathematics. True, some attempt is made to break the monotony in the English and Japanese texts by the introduction of chapters on "investigations" (England) or "topic corners" added to the ends of chapters (Japan). Both of these ideas appear valuable. They introduce different types of activities and, in the case of Japan, provide an opportunity for looking at some aspects of the history of mathematics. One feels, however, that the way in which this is done marginalizes such activities, assigning them to their own little ghetto, where they may well be ignored by teachers. These interpolations aside, very little has been done to break the homogeneity of the texts: to introduce changes of tempo or rhythm. For example, I can recall no passages intended specifically to be read and then discussed by students. An anomaly occurs in the English text: amidst the more routine chapters, there is one on "impossible objects." It is a collection of optical illusions, based in the main on the Penrose ("twisted") triangle and the ("three-pronged") blivet, and illustrated with Escher drawings. The chapter is an interesting combination of work on spatial visualization and model-making in three dimensions, some constructions using ruler and compasses, which demand an accuracy which brings its own reward. Certainly, it stands out from the usual run of chapters in the book. What is puzzling, though, is just what students make of it. As indicated earlier, these English texts provide very few kernels and there are none in this chapter. It would be interesting to know what students see as the chapter's aims, how they believe it differs from other chapters, and what they think they have learned from it. I can imagine some very differing reactions.

Most books also appear to assume a rather unchanging diet of classroom activities. They proceed on a routine of classwork, followed by individual work, and then a class summing-up. Few, for example, assign work to be done by pairs of students or in small groups. This is done most frequently, but then only from time to time, in the U.S. text. Although minor quibbles could be made about the authors'

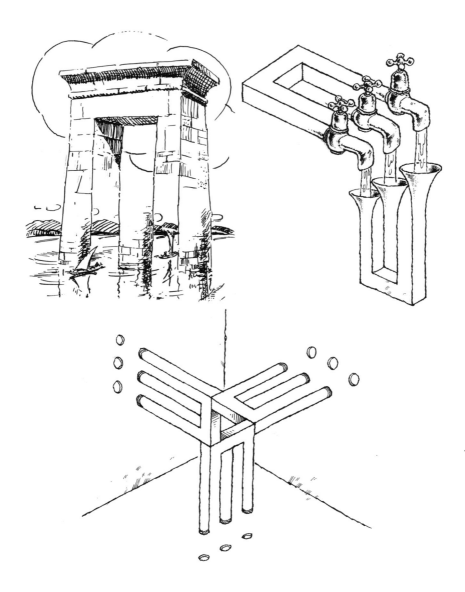

The British text suggests a tantalizing diversion from standard content.

choice of some particular contexts or activities, the general result appears to be one of pure gain.

One result of all this is that the books actively foster only a very limited range of learning strategies: mainly learning by listening and by practising a restricted range of techniques in particular "closed" situations. Learning by reading (except in the case of the English books), by discussion and argument, and in an attempt to acquire the knowledge to solve a problem of one's own choosing are largely ignored. The U.S. text has "independent study" sections in each of its chapters, but these turn out to be merely collections of review exercises. If anything, the impression that one practises independently, but *learns* from a teacher is reinforced. At the end of the book there is a more interesting "independent study handbook." This offers a guide (without examples) to problem-solving. It includes problem-solving strategies, behaviours, and attitudes, strategies for mental arithmetic and estimation, two valuable pages on study skills, notes on how best to work in groups, and then (!) square, square root, and trigonometric tables: an eccentric mixture containing a few plums. I can recall no attempts to encourage students either to criticize or to construct a piece of mathematical text. The emphasis is so frequently on problem-solving where the "problem" is all too often a routine example. This is not an insignificant part of mathematics education, but other aspects require attention also.

A striking feature of all the texts is how little explanation there is of *why* a topic is being studied, other than, perhaps, to solve an arbitrarily imposed problem. Given a good teacher, this omission might be alleviated, but the textbooks in general do little to provide students with an overview of their aims and structure. The important idea that students should be allowed to *appreciate* mathematics and how mathematicians work, as well as demonstrate the acquisition of well-defined operational goals, is ignored. The U.S. texts make some attempt to meet this problem by including a "Welcome" section at the beginning of the book which tells students that:

> Mathematics is valuable and interesting. The next ten pages describe some of the ways your book will help you explore and discover more of the wonders of mathematics.

These U.S. texts provide a "Problem Solving Guide" that students are asked to apply to every question they tackle. Students are urged to "Understand" (the question, the facts, and the key idea); to "Plan and Solve" (by developing a strategy and answering the question); and to "Look Back" (to check their work and propose an alternate solution). It is all rather general, though, and has a somewhat pious air: trust us and keep your excitement within control. The fact that these introductory pages show few textual differences from those introducing the grade 7 book also reinforce the welcome's liturgical tone.

Often the possibilities for doing more already exist within the text, but are ignored in the rush to concentrate on technical performance. Let me give two examples, both inherently good questions taken from the Swiss and French texts respectively.

The first is on primes:

> Every odd number greater than 5 can be expressed as the sum of 3 prime numbers, eg 79 = 47 + 29 + 3. Write as the sum of three primes the numbers 81, 83, 85, 87, 89, 91.

This, on the face of it, is a pedagogically good question. It asks students to recognize primes and by experimentation to find three which sum to the given number. It has the benefit of not having unique answers: students may obtain different but still correct answers to the question, and it encourages teachers to help students develop strategies for extending their results for one given odd number to the next.

What it does not do is establish the initial statement as anything other than a God-given fact. How did mathematicians establish this result? When was this done? By the Greeks or more recently? In fact, the full story is of considerable interest. The "three prime" result for odd numbers was established as recently as 1937 by the Russian mathematician, Vinogradov. However, he was only able to provide a proof for "sufficiently large" odd numbers—and by sufficiently large, he meant very, very large indeed. In 1956, it was shown to be true for numbers with more than six million digits, and, in 1989, Chen and Wang claimed to have proved the theorem for numbers with only tens of thousands of digits.[1] As far as I am aware, the gap between the small numbers which we can readily check and the bound given in

1989 has never been bridged (nor have the calculations giving that bound, or the 1956 one, ever been published). Even in this computer age it would be no easy matter to check the missing odd numbers.

One does not expect 13-year-olds to follow all the logical intricacies of what would constitute a proof of the original statement. Nevertheless, I believe it would be possible to recast the question, in a form appropriate for the range of students for whom it is intended, so as in some way to introduce the notion of proof and the need for it, to establish the fact that there are easily explained conjectures (for example, Goldbach's) that have still to be proved or refuted, to illustrate the international nature of mathematics, and, perhaps most importantly of all, to indicate that there are still *active* mathematicians.

The second example comes from the French text and certainly draws upon the local culture. It presents seven formulae, the first due to Leibniz, for estimating the capacity of a wine barrel, and then asks the students (with the help of calculators) to use them to calculate the capacities of a *barrique* and a *demi-barrique*, given their lengths and major (D) and minor (d) diameters. The students are told the rough capacities of each type of barrel and so can reject some formulae as too approximate.

As an exercise in sticking numbers into formulae it is fine; it also encourages economic calculator procedures. However, it would seem to miss so many opportunities. Why were such formulae developed? If asked to provide a rough formula for the barrel's capacity what would you first suggest? To which shape would you approximate the barrel? Would this be too large or too small an estimate? Between which two bounds does the capacity lie? How might you improve on your first estimate? How would you tackle this problem if you had the calculus at your disposal? Is there an exact formula which would apply to all barrels? What do we want from a formula: for example, how should we balance greater accuracy with ease of use?

Now stand the question on its head and explore the world of dimensions. What happens if we replace D by d everywhere in a formula? How do you explain this? Can we use this as a check to rule out certain possible formulae?

Here we have a multi-faceted example which draws together many ideas from mathematics and its history. It shows how various mathematical models have been created, refined, and/or simplified in answer to a question which at one time was of significance within society.[2] Yet such examples rarely figure in textbooks; all too often exercises focus on a single technique or topic, essentially defined by the "aims" and "content" of the chapter in which they are to be found. The spirit of mathematics is lost when mathematics is seen as the aggregate of disconnected atoms.

Again, these two problems exemplify two driving forces behind mathematics: meeting intellectual challenges and societal needs. This two-pronged motivation does not seem to be strongly enough emphasized in the texts studied here.

Recently, more general interest has been taken in the philosophy of mathematics and its influence on mathematics education (see, for example, Ernest, 1991). However, it is difficult to detect different philosophical positions in the texts considered. The mathematics tends to be presented in a disembodied way, but this is not *logicism* or *formalism* in a mathematical sense. Formal proof is largely absent, as are precise definitions, and only the French and Japanese explicitly attempt to instil the idea of proof. There is, then, little comparison between these books and those produced by Papy and others in the 1960s. The mathematics does not flow inexorably in an axiomatic-deductive manner: indeed, with the exception of the Spanish text, it is usually impossible at the end of one chapter to guess what the content of the next will be. The Spanish text alone is still influenced by the 1960s' attempts to teach algebraic structure. For example, we are told that the integers form a commutative ring with a unit element, but, now there is no formal definition of a ring and no other examples of rings are provided. This is an informal formal approach and, in that respect, would seem to have little of mathematical or pedagogical value to offer. Yet the Spanish text (like all the others) does try to motivate the mathematics by providing contextual examples. Thus, for instance, its chapter on quadratic equations begins with a problem in kinematics concerned with remote-controlled model cars. This rather nice example may serve to motivate and justify the teaching and learning of quadratic equations. (As in all the Spanish chapters, readers are told that at the end of the chapter they will be able to answer the question posed in the chapter's introduction.) However, it tells us nothing about the genesis of quadratic equations or their position within mathematics. Similar examples could be found in all the texts. Motivation, often through contextualization, hides a type of pedagogical formalism.

The passing of the 1960s emphasis on algebraic structure need not be regretted. What is sad is that it has not been replaced by some other clear philosophical or pedagogical structure more appropriate to school mathematics. As presented now, the latter gives the impression of a host of content items somewhat tenuously linked and motivated. One can admire certain chapters or threads, much in the way that one admires the architecture of a particular building, but "town-planning" seems largely absent. Occasionally, as in the French texts, a university mathematician can see the foundations being carefully laid for future work (such as in the restricted definition of a linear function [map] which will permit an easy extension to the notion of a linear transformation), but this subtlety will, one fears, pass the student and most teachers by. What appears to be missing is any attempt to organize the curriculum around well-defined mathematical themes crossing the arithmetic-algebra-geometry divides and to use these to help provide students with a structural framework for their learning—and also to support teachers in their teaching. A first attempt to establish such a framework of "recurring themes" has been made by Gardiner (1992). It is an idea which deserves further consideration, development, and elaboration.

The Pedagogical Structure of the Texts

Three important issues associated with any text—to which very different responses are demonstrated in the books studied—are:

1. For what population of students is the book written?

2. Within that range, what attempts, if any, are made to deal with students of varying ability?

3. How are the mathematical topics organized/presented during the year?

Of the books studied, those from France, Japan, Spain, and the U.S. are expected to be used by students drawn from the whole of the ability range. Even then there are sometimes essential differences within the national school structures with important consequences for authors. In France, for example, considerable use is made of retention, that is, requiring pupils to repeat a year if they have failed to perform satisfactorily (about one in three pupils at grade 8 has repeated a year at some time [Min. de l'Education, 1994, p.96]), whereas this is seldom done in Japan or the U.S. Different assumptions, therefore, will need to be made about the attainments and abilities of students entering the grade. In Japan and the U.S., both attainments and abilities will cover a wide range. In France, the range in attainment will be more restricted, but that in ability will be just as wide.

The Netherlands has a multi-partite educational system in which students are divided at age 12 into four streams: pre-university, higher general, intermediate general, and lower vocational. The book studied was intended for students in the lower two streams (which at the time of its publication contained the median student). In Berne, students are divided into two streams of roughly equal size; again, the text for the lower stream has been selected. England has a mainly comprehensive system but also a national curriculum which assumes that eighth-graders will have progressed through that curriculum at very different rates. Although published some years before the imposition of a national curriculum, the SMP series makes similar assumptions and offers four levels of texts at this grade: yellow (high attainers), blue, green, and amber. (At grade 9, a "red" series is interpolated between yellow and blue, and is intended to help "late developers" to convert from the blue to the yellow course.) Differentiation takes place within a school or even a class. It should be observed that although the Netherlands and Swiss texts studied are intended for the "lower half" of the ability range and so only just "catch" the median student, this is not the case for the SMP blue series. This is used by, roughly, 40% of the cohort distributed almost evenly about the 55th percentile. Norway is more truly comprehensive. However, in addition to its "general" book, it also offers an "alternative version" which contains the same main core (thus facilitating upwards transitions), but omits some of the more difficult work.

There were no obvious hints on differentiation within the texts from Japan, Spain, Switzerland, and the U.S. However, the French text marked some questions as being trickier, and supplied hints to these, while the Netherlands and Norwegian texts had symbols indicating the relative difficulty of particular problems. Since the Netherlands text was intended for two streams whose mathematical needs would soon diverge, it contains notes in the preliminary pages providing instructions for pupils and teachers on how to deal with differentiation, including work and examples that might be omitted. Such advice is more normally given in teachers' guides. The U.S. teachers' guide suggests that the class periods devoted to a chapter should be allocated in different ways according to the "track" concerned, implying that, unlike in Japan, for example, students will be setted into classes by ability and attainment. A typical example is:

| | Track | | |
Activity type	Basic	Average	Enriched
Core	7	7	7
Problem-solving, enrichment	1	2	3
Extra practice, reviews, reteaching	3	2	1

Users of the French text hardly require guidance, for its chapter structure tells all. The standard pattern is:

Activities: Individual or in small groups.

Essentials: Kernels and key worked examples.

Exercises: *"Savoir faire"*—practising basic techniques and skills. *"Chercher"*—more open and contextualized problems drawing upon cross-curricular and societal links; programmer's corner.

Clearly, as in the U.S. where such divisions of exercises exist but are not so starkly drawn, higher attaining pupils are likely to spend more time on interesting problems while those lower down the ability range will try to ensure they acquire the basic techniques.

It is possible, then, that in some French and U.S. classrooms, the average and below average students will be offered a rather thin diet of basics with little in the way of enrichment, cross-curricular work, or excitement (although both books offer more opportunities for these than do the texts from Japan, the Netherlands, Norway, Spain, and Switzerland).

Whether or not this is a price worth paying to avoid the early labelling of students as "good," "bad," or "indifferent" is not an easy question to answer, especially if one wishes to do so on the basis of firm data, in the form of results on, for example, comparative attainment, the longitudinal progression of individuals within cohorts, subsequent employment opportunities, and the views of students and parents, rather than on an emotive gut reaction. Certainly, the median English student is likely to be presented with a more extensive diet in terms of a range of activities and interesting topics. But he or she, as a result, will lack the technical mathematical skills of many continental peers (to say nothing of Japanese students).

Even in England, though, differences between the various SMP coloured series extend beyond mathematical content and depth of treatment. There are differences in the language used, the balance between text and graphics, and the contexts from which examples are drawn. This has led Dowling (1991) to argue that mathematical attainment and ability are being used to introduce and/or perpetuate deep-rooted class divisions. His work lacks a longitudinal aspect to check whether the materials for low attainers actually attempt over time to alleviate problems apparent on the students' entry to grade 8, or whether they merely reinforce them (see Howson, 1993). Nevertheless, it draws attention to an interesting sociological aspect of mathematics education which merits further research.

Indeed, the whole area of differentiation, how it is being dealt with and its effects, is seriously under-researched, particularly since it is such an emotive and politically weighty issue. In particular, the role of textual materials in alleviating difficulties both for students and teachers demands attention.

Similar wide disparities of practice can also be observed when one considers how mathematical content is delivered, both within a single year and over a period of years. Thus if we consider the number of chapters included in grade 8 texts we find:

England	27
France	17
Japan (all series)	8
Netherlands *	13
Norway	14
Spain	29
Switzerland	9
U.S.	14

* The Netherlands text includes a review chapter.

Some differences can be explained away by the manner in which "units" are aggregated. Indeed, despite these data, the Spanish text has more in common with the Japanese than with the English. Seven consecutive chapters on the rationals ("addition of ...", "subtraction of ...", "addition and subtraction of ...", etc.) might just have well have been placed in one chapter with appropriate sections. The important factor here is more the amount of continuous classroom time devoted to the study of a particular topic. Some idea of the differences of approach and weighting is provided by the following table, bearing in mind that it is not always easy to classify a chapter as either "algebra" or "arithmetic" and that one must, therefore, resort to multiple coding. The Japanese, for example, classify "linear functions" under arithmetic rather than algebra, as I have done here. See the discussions of arithmetic and algebra in chapter 3.

Table 2.1 illustrates very different philosophies and weightings. There is also a clear dichotomy between those countries in which the texts present this topic in one chunk (France, Japan, and Spain, a semester or a whole year respectively in the case of the two last), and those which offer students a more varied diet and take up algebraic topics on various occasions throughout the year. (I am told that in

Table 2.1: Placing and Percentage of Chapters Devoted to Algebra

	No. of chapters	Algebra chapter numbers	Percentage of total
England	27	(Part 1) 12, (Part 2) 8, 10	11
France	17	4-6	18
Japan	8	1-4	50
Netherlands	13	3, 6, 10, 11, 13	38
Norway	14	9, 10, 13	21
Spain	29	1-29	100
Switzerland	9	3, 7	22
United States	14	4, 15	14

France the chapter order of the texts is not necessarily followed in the classrooms and that it would be dangerous to infer that, for example, algebra is always taught in one block.)

It must be emphasized that the Spanish book is written for a syllabus which is now being superseded. The new curriculum will encourage the study of a wider range of mathematics in each grade. Moreover, much of what is covered in the Spanish text would, given less emphasis on algebraic structure, be classified as arithmetic. The SMP text clearly indicates the feelings of the authors concerning the emphasis on algebra appropriate for the median student—another interesting aspect of the "differentiation" discussion.

The advantages and disadvantages of the "block" system as opposed to the rapidly "spiralling" one have been discussed elsewhere (see, for example, McKnight et al., 1987). From the point of view of learning, "short bursts" allied to "long gaps" will present difficulties. Moreover, as will be seen in chapter 3, the number of mathematical topics touched upon in, for example, the grade 8 U.S. text is far greater than that for any of the corresponding Japanese books. However, extra-mathematical considerations, including the need to provide variety for those students who lack strong motivation, may rule out the Japanese approach.

An allied problem is that of review and revision. The need for review is met in different ways: for example, SMP interpolate "review exercises" every four chapters or so, whereas the Netherlands has a final "revision chapter," and the U.S. a cumulative review test and then a "review" (which deals only with elementary arithmetic, the metric system, the classification of triangles and congruent triangles, and so paints a most dismal picture of where its priorities lie and/or what it expects students to take with them into grade 9).

In addition to the problem of "review" within and over a year, there is also a larger problem. A striking feature of the Japanese text is the absence of work on arithmetic—that has been "done." Moreover, there is no obvious attempt to incorporate review of key concepts, such as percentage, into the new material. This omission looks somewhat singular unless students in Japan have retentive powers not possessed by their peers elsewhere. At the other extreme, the U.S. texts repeat much work from grade to grade and, indeed, some pages of the final "skills review" for the grade 7 text occur almost unchanged in that section of the grade 8 text.

We have already commented on the degree of teacher autonomy allowed by the texts: great in the case of Switzerland, less so in other countries. What is perhaps particularly noteworthy about the Japanese texts is that they provide not only a large-scale structure for the year—for they are finely attuned both to the syllabus and the amount of time available for mathematics teaching—but underpinning this is a well-defined lesson structure. (We have already referred to the aim of "trying to provide one kernel a lesson.") Other texts do not have so tight a structure. Paradoxically, this would not seem to result in greater teacher autonomy, for it would often appear easier to replace the text's approach to a particular topic in the Japanese classroom than in some others in which the "flow" of a topic would be expected to extend over several lessons.

Another key question, which we have already mentioned, concerns the provision of exercises. Here, a major difference between countries lies in the provision, or not, of supplementary student work or activity books. These, for example, are supplied with the Norwegian, Japanese, and (although it may seem hard to believe, granted the length of the pupils' text) U.S. books. Clearly, the use of such supplementary materials will affect the emphasis on practice and the acquisition of techniques—or even on more advanced problem-solving. It has not been possible to take these supplementary texts into account. Moreover, comparison between countries is bedevilled by the fact that few topics are actually taught in grade 8 in more than three or four countries (see chapter 3). One topic which provides some useful data is that of the multiplication and division of integers. This is included in the French, Netherlands, Norwegian, Spanish, and U.S. texts. It is not covered in the English texts for the median student (who stops at addition and subtraction of negative numbers) or in the corresponding Swiss text. However, it is covered in the English text for high attainers.

The differences are significant. In the English text for high-attainers there are some 60 or so formal operations to be evaluated in order to check that students have understood the way in which the signs combine. (The English text is unique in using an "upper" negative sign to indicate that we are dealing with a negative number. This allows for a clear distinction to be made between, say, the integer, "negative one," and the unary operation, "subtract one.") Examples are then given on substitution into formulae and the solution of equations. Practice is also provided on using the calculator. The French make more use of the calculator and lay greater stress on the rules, but have far fewer formal exercises. As elsewhere in the French text, exercises are often translated into puzzles in an attractive way: magic squares, magic honeycombs, and examples such as "given -5, -2, 1000 and -3, can you combine these, using the four arithmetical operations, to obtain 103?" There are some contextualized questions involving, for example, average temperatures, but these do not make use of the multiplication of negative integers. The Netherlands make use of formal examples (similar to England, but now with some in the form "complete ... x 8 = -64) and also exercises on mappings in the coordinate plane and graphs. As an option they include work on equations and on powers of negative numbers. Norway provides very many formal exercises similar to those in the Netherlands text; powers are not introduced, but inequalities are, such as "what can you say about xy given that $x > 0$ and $y < 0$?" There is little attempt to put such calculations in context. Spain puts little emphasis on formal calculations (the book as a whole is stronger on formal kernels than on exercises, on "knowing that" rather than doing), but introduces ideas of parity and, as elsewhere in the book, asks questions of the type "deduce what would be the sign of an expression obtained by multiplying a number of negative factors." The chapter ends with a contextualized example on the use of negative numbers in a code inspired by Edgar Allan Poe's *The Gold Bug*. The U.S. follows France and Spain in having relatively few formal examples. It attempts little in the way of contextualized examples, but asks for a counter-example concerning closure under division of the integers, and for rules concerning the signs of powers of -3 and of negative numbers in general.

There are, then, great differences in the number of repetitive, formal exercises set in the texts, even though this is a well-defined topic introducing a relatively straightforward technique. Although calculators are much used in the English, French, and U.S. texts, the Netherlands and Norwegian texts do not employ them specifically in their chapters on the integers, and the Spanish do not use them at all. There is unanimity in finding it hard to construct contextualized examples which justify the teaching of the multiplication and division of integers. I cannot recall any text specifically referring to the mathematician's general wish to try to extend operations defined on one set of elements to a larger set, or indeed giving any specific explanation of why this mathematical topic was being considered at that particular time. The ways in which multiplication of integers are introduced/defined differed greatly and these will be described in the discussion of arithmetic in chapter 3.

Notes

[1] The first numerical bound on "sufficiently large" was given by Borozdkin, who, in 1956, reduced this to that quoted in the text. Chen and Wang published the latest bound (e to the power [e to the power 11.503]) in *Acta Math. Sinica* 32 (1989). I am much indebted to Dr. Roger Heath-Brown of Oxford University for helping me to sort out the history of this topic.

[2] The problem of gauging, as it was then known, was a major one in the eighteenth and early nineteenth centuries when the volume of barrels had to be calculated for customs and other purposes. Many books were written at that time on the subject and numerous formulae were produced. For example, Hutton's *Mensuration* gives many examples, but in his 1815 *Mathematical and Philosophical Dictionary* he restricts himself to giving only his favourite (!) rule (which, not surprisingly, is not one quoted in the French text):

> Add into one sum,
> 39 times the square of the bung diameter [D]
> 25 times the square of the head diameter [d]
> 26 times the product of these diameters;
> multiply the sum by the length of the cask
> and the product by the number .00034;
> then this last number divided by 9 will give the wine gallons, and
>   divided by 11 will give the ale gallons.

These calculations assume all measurements are made in inches. Note also that a gallon of wine was not the same as a gallon of ale.

In order to make life easier, gauging rods with sliding scales were produced which could be inserted diagonally from the bung. The measurements so taken could then be used to find the volume of the barrel. The geometric and arithmetical problems to be solved in the production of such rods were by no means straightforward.

Chapter 3

Close-up on the Texts: Contents & Aims

Nowadays national curricula are not, in general, simply lists of content. They usually also contain lists of processes which it is hoped students will acquire. National texts give us indications of the extent to which these hopes are actually and actively sought. Once again, it is not possible to infer that what is in the text will, in fact, be attempted, or, for that matter, that activities not contained in the texts will not be encouraged within classrooms. Nevertheless, texts provide a guide to what educators believe is possible/desirable and how goals might be attained.

Mathematizing

The English national curriculum[1] has an attainment target, "Using and Applying Mathematics," which can well be taken as representative of general aims in this area. This target is further subdivided into three strands: applications; mathematical communication; and reasoning, logic, and proof.

The first strand is an important one in that it asks students to learn how to apply mathematics, as distinct from learning about the applications of mathematics. It sets extremely ambitious goals, and not ones that have been frequently sought before. Thus the median student at age 16 (and the higher-attainer at 12 or so) is expected to be capable of "designing a task and selecting the mathematics and other resources; checking information and obtaining any that is missing; using 'trial and improvement' methods." Exactly what this means is a matter for the English to ponder. What is clear from reading these texts, however, is that at the moment little is being done to encourage the growth of such powers. In general, students are presented with tasks, rather than asked to design them, and the context in which the task is presented usually defines the mathematics which is expected to be brought to bear upon it in the hope of finding a solution. A half-way house, which perhaps offers a feasible way in which gradually to proceed towards the English goal, is offered by the U.S. text. Each chapter commences with an activity related to the main content of the chapter. The chapter on measurement in geometry, for example, begins by giving data on Ayers Rock including its circumference. The students are then asked to estimate the distance around their school building, to devise a method to approximate the perimeter, to use this to obtain an estimate, and to discuss the different methods used and to compare the results. Such open-ended tasks remain the exception, as do those encouraging "differentiation by outcome" which allow students of different abilities to answer questions at a variety of levels appropriate to their knowledge and attainments.

This task also takes us some way towards meeting the second of the English goals: that of learning how to communicate mathematics and to discuss it and its outcomes with others. Examples have already been given of other ways in which this goal can be encouraged: the English investigations (which, of course, have to be written up), the smaller Spanish questions which demand explanations not merely numbers and operations on them, and, of course, the more demanding proofs sought by the French and Japanese. As remarked earlier, these books do not pay specific attention to the need to train students to read mathematics. The development of communication skills cannot, however, be detached from the manner in which classes are taught. There has been a tradition in Germany of using class discussion with individual contributions from students as a basis of class teaching—a tradition also found in Japan. In England, however, more emphasis has tended to be placed on individual "deskwork" by students and there is usually less discussion between pupils and between pupils and teacher. Such teaching traditions will frequently outweigh the efforts of textbooks to promote communication skills.

The problem of "proof" is a major one. Only two countries make a specific attempt to teach proof in a formal sense: France and Japan. In both cases they select geometry as the principal vehicle. Both also depart from Euclid. We shall consider their approaches later in this chapter. It suffices here to indicate that the relevant chapters display a marked increase in the cognitive demands made of students. Nevertheless, both represent serious attempts to deal with, and to introduce students to, a central aspect of mathematics. The U.S. chapter, "Mathematical Reasoning," is the last in a long book and is both perfunctory (see, for example, its section on compound logical statements) and highly demanding in many of the tasks it sets. The Spanish occasionally provide formal proofs, such as using associativity and commutativity to show that multiplying the numerator and denominator of a fraction by a constant yields an equivalent fraction, but (not surprisingly) do not expect students to produce such proofs. Elsewhere, it is perhaps easier to find examples of what the English curriculum describes as "making and testing generalisations and simple hypotheses [for example, on powers of negative numbers]; defining and reasoning in simple contexts with some precision" ['some' presumably being one of the undefined terms!]; and "following a chain of mathematical reasoning; spotting inconsistencies."

It would be wrong, however, to leave the impression that the need to encourage broader types of mathematical activities is altogether ignored. As we have already stressed, the U.S. text attempts to meet the challenges set out in the NCTM *Standards*; and the Norwegians, for example, have an early chapter, "Problem Solving," which looks specifically at experimenting, problems with several solutions, and open-ended problems. Yet, so often these responses appear to be "tokens": a nod has been made in a particular direction and now we can get back to good, solid mathematics teaching that everyone recognizes and accepts. This is not a surprising course of action to take! Some teachers have yet to be convinced that many of the new aims are actually desirable, and many more, whilst recognizing their desirability, need convincing that they are feasible. Textbooks alone are unlikely to supply any such conviction: this will only come with the help of other forms of in-service education. Moreover, it has still to be effectively demonstrated that such aims are attainable once one moves outside a small group of dedicated and highly motivated teachers unencumbered by the tight constraints of an assessment and evaluation system.

Textbooks are important educational instruments, but their power for significantly influencing classroom practice and teachers' beliefs should not be overestimated.

Applications of Mathematics

It will have already been noted that all countries are now making far greater efforts to present students with exercises set in a "real-world" context. The percentage of word problems to be found in texts has increased, in some cases enormously, although Spain still lags behind other countries. Some years ago (Howson et al., 1981), I quoted Edmund Burke's *Reflections on the French Revolution* ("not one reference whatsoever ... to anything moral or anything politic; nothing that relates to the concerns, the actions, the passions, the interests of men") and added that he could well have been reviewing a French modern mathematics text. Practices have now changed, and, indeed, nowhere more so than in France, for this French text provides an extremely rich and varied collection of exercises in contexts drawn from the physical, natural, and social sciences, art and architecture, and day-to-day life.

This emphasis on contextualization and social relevance is by no means new (see Howson, 1982, 1989). The original books in English and German (Recorde, 1543, et seq., and Ries, 1522), for example, were intended to be read by those who wished to use arithmetic (and other mathematical topics) for commercial purposes and so made use of appropriate real-life examples.[2] Indeed, as the mathematician Wallis was later to write (see Howson, 1982, p. 34), this resulted in mathematics being "scarce looked upon as Academical studies, but rather Mechanical; as the business of Traders, Merchants, Seamen, Carpenters, Surveyors ... or the like." This dichotomy between the academically esteemed and the utilitarian has persisted and has been the subject of many swings, particularly since education became institutionalized.

Some of the problems to which contextualization gives rise were addressed by De Morgan in an 1831 article, *On Mathematical Instruction.* In particular, he drew attention to two specific problems: the likely reaction of students to exercises and examples that were "set" in real-life contexts but bore no relation to what actually happens in reality (for example, do people ever find the value of a horse by solving a pair of linear simultaneous equations?); and the danger that if mathematics is presented and motivated simply as a utilitarian subject then it will be devalued and misrepresented in the process.

These problems are still with us and I have already remarked on the need to show how mathematics arises in response to both intellectual and societal challenges. The intellectual aspect is now perhaps under-emphasized, although clearly the younger student is more likely to be motivated by the utilitarian aspects. But attempts to put mathematics in context are more often motivated by the justified and educationally desirable goal of helping students develop the skill to model a particular (frequently contrived) situation in mathematical terms (and, usually, using the mathematical techniques currently being acquired) than to exhibit societal problems, the solution of which can be expedited, or even made possible, by mathematical means. Perhaps the eighth grade is too early to expect to see serious attempts made to demonstrate how mathematics is actually used within society. Certainly, for example, whilst welcoming the U.S. chapter, "Consumer Topics," one wonders just how many eighth-graders will be fired by its opening problem—working out how much a stockbroker makes a year in basic salary plus commission. (Again, we see how examples and exercises can show class and social bias. Ensuring that texts are not dominated by a "middle class" ethos is far from easy.) Consideration of compound interest and hire purchase (installment buying) together with the arithmetic of credit cards might also be deferred to a time when it is more likely to be of relevance. The cost of keeping a dog (an old favourite) and of preparing for Christmas, both used by Norway, may well create more interest. Such "homely" examples can, of course, be found in other texts. In particular, the Swiss text makes good use of data drawn from a variety of local sources including some on sports such as ski-jumping and gymnastics, which provide plenty of opportunities for practice in adding, dividing, and ordering decimals.

Where the Norwegian text is particularly distinguished is in its use of environmental and social examples which are to be found at the end of each chapter (often only tenuously connected to the chapter's theme). Two of its chapters conclude with exercises applying mathematics to issues connected with the world's oil reserves. For example,chapter 2 concludes with the following exercise:

Exercise: "The World's Oil Reserves"
The table below shows how much oil there is in the oil sources in four of the world's highest producing countries. The table also shows how much oil these countries produce each year.

Country	Oil Reserves (million tonnes)	Production per Year (million tonnes)
Saudi Arabia	20 000	450
Kuwait	9 000	90
Soviet Union	7 000	550
Iran	6 500	285

a) Calculate how long the oil production can continue unchanged in each of the four countries before the sources are used up.

b) If the production per year is reduced by 10%, how long would it take before the sources are used up in each country?

For discussion in class:
What different sources of energy are we using?
What are the conflicts due to oil production?
What could happen when the world's oil sources are used up?

Attention is also focused in the Norwegian textbook on such issues as the energy demands of a range of household appliances, differences in population density and the provision of food, water, education, and health care in different continents, radioactive fallout, and traffic offences and accidents. One imagines that these will interest more eighth-grade students than will hire purchase (important though this latter topic is).

Yet such examples do not illustrate how mathematics is used to *solve* problems: for the solutions to environmental and societal problems will almost certainly depend upon other considerations—and that will not be lost on students. What mathematics allows us to do is to describe and quantify and so to clarify issues, a point insufficiently well made in the texts. When claiming utilitarian virtues for mathematics we must not weaken our case by claiming too much for the subject—there is no need for bogus arguments. However, this would seem to imply the need for a greater emphasis to be placed on the "appreciation" of how mathematics contributes to society. This might mean the inclusion in texts of descriptive accounts unconstrained by the needs that they should depend upon the basic techniques currently being taught or provide a context for the setting of yet more exercises. Such an initiative might prove a significant contribution towards the attainment of affective goals.

Technology

It will already have become apparent that there are still differences between countries concerning the degree to which calculators are integrated into the teaching at the grade 8 level. England, France, the Netherlands, Norway, and the U.S. expect them to be used. Switzerland and Spain do not (although their use may be permitted in classrooms). In the larger TIMSS survey, the commentator from Japan lists the use of calculators as regular but not essential. However, I cannot recall any specific calculator-related work in the Japanese texts. The Norwegian text, incidentally, provides an introduction to the calculator from which one infers that this is the first grade in which they are used; in other countries familiarity with a calculator appears to be assumed. In general, the calculator is used to carry the heavier arithmetical burdens. One clear influence of the calculator on the curriculum is the early introduction of compound interest in the U.S. The

French, in their section on the use of the "reciprocal" key, take the opportunity to introduce such applications as the rule for working out the effect of two resistances in parallel (although that other old physics favourite, on image and object distances in optics, fails to make an appearance). In the section on trigonometry the French make use of the calculator to find not only cosines of acute angles, but also inverse cosines. In contrast, the U.S. text initially lays stress on the use of trigonometric tables, but then includes some calculator work on tangents. Another general influence on the curriculum which could be ascribed to the use of calculators is the increased emphasis on scientific notation. Again, calculator use increases the need for work on estimation and this is recognized with varying degrees of conviction. There are a few examples, such as the introduction of the multiplication of negative integers, where the calculator has led to changes in teaching methods. (See the discussion of arithmetic below.)

There are no references to graphic calculators. This is understandable since they are relative late-comers to the market and, although their use is now expected in some senior high school courses, their price has not dropped sufficiently for them to be considered essential equipment within the grade 8 classroom. Yet at this level there are many topics in algebra and co-ordinate geometry (see the discussions of algebra and geometry in this chapter) which would benefit enormously from their use.

Two texts make reference to computers: the French and the U.S. In both cases, however, they remain peripheral and not central to the teaching/learning process. One gains the impression that the texts' authors had limited expectations concerning the possible take-up of these passages. Here again, though, time and availability of hardware are key factors. SMP is the oldest of the texts studied and in the early 1980s ready access to computers in the classroom could not be assumed. Since then, SMP has, for example, produced supplementary materials including software (although for the most part it has simply recommended existing examples) and the teachers' guides *Using BASIC, Using LOGO,* and *Using Software.*

The titles of these guides immediately suggest a possible dichotomy of aims. Is the emphasis to be on helping students to construct simple programs in an appropriately chosen programming language, or is it to be on acquainting them with the use of commercially produced software? The two texts which use computers follow different paths. That the French entitle their computer sections "Programmer's Corner" tells all. Here, computing means the implementation, modification, and production of simple programs (up to 10 lines or so) written in BASIC. The U.S. text, on the other hand, concentrates on the use of software, such as spreadsheets. In both cases, however, the resulting emphasis is on the use of computers in the teaching and learning of number, rather than space and geometry.

No doubt emphases will change in the coming years. Nevertheless, it seems strange that the newly-produced French text should have this particular bias when, for so many mathematics educators, French work on computers in schools is linked with the use of specific software, Cabri-Géométrie, for the teaching of geometry (see, for example, Laborde, 1994). Certainly, I believe that in future the emphasis will become more firmly placed on the use of software and that programming will be viewed as a more recondite art to be left to specialists. However, the need to ensure that precise *mathematical* goals are being served will still exist: I could not always discern a clear mathematical point in some of the U.S. examples.

Arithmetic

Table 3.1 which indicates arithmetical topics covered in the various texts shows considerable differences existing between countries in what is taught at grade 8. Here, however, it is essential to emphasize two points. The texts from England, the Netherlands, and Switzerland are those intended for median students and so omit work which will be being studied by the more able. Also, the English text will be used by some students who in the Netherlands or Switzerland would use the texts for high-ability students, and other, less ambitious texts are used by English students in the lower third of the ability range. The second is that formal primary education in Norway begins at age 7 and the average age of entry to Swiss primary schools is 6 years and 10 months. This means that Norwegian and Swiss students will have received roughly one year less formal schooling than their peers in other countries and this must be taken into account when studying Table 3.1 and other such tables. English children begin primary school at age 5, a possible advantage off-set by the haphazard and limited provision of pre-primary education in that country.

As noted earlier, the Japanese pay no special attention to arithmetic in this grade although of necessity there is some review of arithmetical work, particularly that on fractions. Square roots, rationals, irrationals, and primes are taught in grade 9. With these exceptions, the topics listed in Table 3.1 have been covered in earlier grades (see Howson, 1991, which contains details of the Japanese national curriculum).

We also note differences in the extent to which operations on the integers are introduced. In addition to the different emphases on exercises on these (see chapter 2), countries introduce these in different ways. It is perhaps illuminating to take one topic, for example, the multiplication of integers, and to see how introductions vary.[3] Some years ago, the poet W.H. Auden (see Griffiths and Howson, 1974, p. 258) explained how, at his 9-13 school, he was taught:

> Minus times minus equals plus;
> the reason for this we need not discuss.

This at least resulted in his remembering the kernel, and possibly encouraged him to become a poet, on the grounds that he could not do much worse.

Spain follows a similar, but less poetic and more convoluted course: "the product of two integers is another integer having as its absolute value the product of the absolute values of the two factors. Its sign is positive if the signs of the two factors are similar and negative if the two factors have different signs." France asks students to see what happens when two directed numbers having different signs are multiplied on a calculator, and then if the two numbers have the same sign: an up-to-date interpretation of *deus ex machina*. The U.S. text complements this approach with pattern spotting, a method used also by the Norwegians. Thus, $(-2) \times 3$ is defined by repeated addition and then the pattern $(-2) \times 3$, $(-2) \times 2$, $(-2) \times 1$, ... is extended. This

Table 3.1: Arithmetical Topics

Topic	E	F	Ne	No	Sp	Sw	U.S.
Fractions, decimals	●				●		●
Fractions: operations on		●		●	●	●	●
Decimals: operations on	●			●		●	●
Rounding and sig. figures	●		●	●		●	●
Rational and irrational numbers						●	●
Integers: addition and subtraction	●		●	●	●	○	●
Multiplication and division		●	●	●	●		●
Distributivity, associativity			●			●	●
BODMAS (order of operations)		●		○		●	●
Percentages	●			●		●	●
Ratio and proportion	●	●				●	●
Powers (exponents)			●	●	●	●	●
Scientific notation		●				○	●
Square roots			●		●	●	●
Primes and factorization					●	●	●
GCD (HCF) and LCM						●	●
Sequences							●
Interest, hire purchase							●
Time and timetables	●			●			●
Calculators	●	●	●	●			●

E (England), F (France), Ne (Netherlands), No (Norway), Sp (Spain), Sw (Switzerland), U.S. (United States)

● Topics covered   ○ Topics only lightly covered

Note: Japan does not treat arithmetical topics in this grade.

provides a degree of justification, particularly if illustrated by a graph. England (high attainers) and the Netherlands provide models. The English consider the combination of dilatations (enlargements) with positive and negative scale-factors, a model appropriate for multiplication but not for addition (it is, in fact, a much restricted version of the Gaussian model for operations on the complex numbers). The Netherlands text uses the same "contextualized" model for both operations. As is so often the case, the model is (mathematically) appropriate for addition, but not for multiplication. Unfortunately, however, in this instance a mathematical fudge is built upon scientific nonsense. I am told, however, that this "witch's cauldron" model[4] is traditional in the Netherlands. Nevertheless, one wonders if the means adopted to provide students with a context within which they can recover the rules for operating with negative numbers are really any more pedagogically and philosophically satisfying than, or as effective in prompting the memory as, Auden's poem.

This example, taken together with the remarks on exercises in chapter 2, should warn us of the dangers in believing that if a topic is introduced in several countries then it is always treated in the same manner and with the same degree of emphasis.

Bearing this in mind, it is relatively easy to interpret Table 3.1. The way in which topics are hierarchically arranged usually allows us to deduce whether or not a topic has been treated in an earlier grade. However, it is necessary to warn that there is a degree of subjectivity in this and succeeding tables: a subjective decision has to be taken on whether or not a mention and the inclusion of a number of exercises means that the subject has been "taught" and, if so, has the treatment been "light."

Attention may be drawn to the way in which France tends better to link arithmetical ratio and proportion with algebraic linear maps and geometric similarity and trigonometry. I was surprised by the emphasis given in several countries to conventions governing the order in which operations are to be carried out in unbracketed expressions. This was known in England by the mnemonic, BODMAS, before this topic was dropped in favour of encouraging the universal use of brackets. The point here would seem to be an important pedagogical one: should we at this stage be encouraging transparency of meaning and thought, achieved in this case through the use of brackets (parentheses), or emphasizing conventions which permit us to write expressions in a condensed form? A pilot TIMSS item which asked students to evaluate a bracketed expression was rejected by at least one country as too easy and it was suggested that it should be stiffened by removing the brackets. This reaction raises serious problems for me concerning the teaching, learning, and appeal of mathematics.

Several countries touch upon primes and the factorization of numbers. Spain alone goes where experience of teaching at university level would make me fear to tread: it defines primes on the integers. A number a is prime if and only if its set of divisors is $\{1, -1, a, -a\}$. The first example given of a prime is -13, and what happens when the text deals with factorization is left to the reader's imagination.

Spain and the U.S. also introduce the concept of rational and irrational numbers. This is not very successfully accomplished: "decimals that do not terminate or repeat are called *irrational numbers*" is not a good working definition. How does one check that $\sqrt{2}$ and π are irrational? We are told that both of them are, but alas, with no hint as to how and when these results were arrived at. A section on computing with irrational numbers is based on "multiplying" surds on a calculator. The limits which a calculator places on the types of number it can deal with are ignored. These topics might well have been deferred until they could have been given a more satisfactory treatment; it is difficult to envisage what has been gained by their inclusion. Yet, despite these criticisms, the U.S. chapter on rational and irrational numbers contains much that is very good, for example, sections on scientific notation, number-sense, and calculator and spreadsheet use.

Another noteworthy point is that two countries with differentiated systems, England and the Netherlands, do not introduce operations on fractions at this stage. This is an example of a "content" decision that lies at the heart of the debate on differentiation.

Finally, it is noticeable that the Swiss clearly distinguish between a fraction as an operator ("one half of") and as a number (1/2). Such a distinction becomes particularly important when one moves on to percentages. Davis (1992) has complained of the confusing way in which U.S. texts (as do some others) treat percentages as pure numbers. Certainly, examples such as "Is 5/9 greater than 100%?" justify his complaints: "Is '5/9 of' greater than '100% of'?" would seem less confusing and more appropriate. Is it time to give precision and unambiguity a chance? After all, traditional sloppiness has not proved very successful.

Algebra

As Table 3.2 indicates, the range of algebraic topics taught at grade 8 is rather limited. There is a concentration of effort on formulae and their graphs. Often these are linear expressions but not always. Area and volume formulae provide obvious exceptions and there are others drawn from the sciences (for example, that for resistances in parallel). The solution of linear equations is a common topic (in those countries where it has not already been tackled). Only Spain provides a full treatment of quadratic equations, but other countries, such as the Netherlands and Norway, provide simple examples of these. It is surprising to find a chapter on biquadratic equations in the Spanish grade 8 text.

Spain still introduces some of the jargon of algebraic structure but the approach is half-hearted. The authors appear to be doing their best (which is not, alas, sufficient) to make an impossible syllabus accessible. Thus rationals are not defined formally in terms of equivalence classes of ordered pairs of integers, as they might have been in a New Math text. Instead the set of all fractions is partitioned into subsets of mutually equivalent fractions, without equivalence relations and classes being formally defined. A distinction is drawn (but thankfully soon abandoned) between the fraction 1/2 and the rational number {1/2} which, one hopes, is appreciated by the students.

Little is now taught on sets. Spain uses the language and one infers that they have been introduced in an earlier grade, and Switzerland and the U.S. have sections on them. The U.S. work is contained in a chapter on mathematical reasoning which considers Venn diagrams and, like the Swiss, some simple combinatorial applications, before moving on to compound logical statements. This section is particularly demanding. "If ... then" would hardly seem to be material to be polished off in half a page, and if I wished to introduce the idea of a truth table to students then that for "if ... then" would certainly not be my first choice. Indeed, it is hard to see what the text's objectives are at this point. An advance organizer, such as the question mentioned earlier on inequalities ("what can be said about xy if x > 0 and ... ?"), is an important pedagogical tool. I recall that in a

Table 3.2: Algebraic Topics

Topic	Country							
	E	F	J	Ne	No	Sp	Sw	U.S.
Formulae	●	●	●	●	●			●
Graphs for formulae	●	●	●	●	●			●
Linear equations	●			●	●	●	●	●
Equations and inequalities		●	●	●			○	
Linear (affine) maps (y = mx + c)		●	●		●	●		
Polynomials: addition and subtraction			●		○	●		
Remainder theorem						●		
Simultaneous linear equations			●			●		
Algebraic structure						●		
Quadratic equations						●		
Biquadratic equations						●		
Sets							●	●

E (England), F (France), J (Japan), Ne (Netherlands), No (Norway), Sp (Spain), Sw (Switzerland), U.S. (United States)

● Topics covered   ○ Topics only lightly covered

textbook series which I edited in the 1960s we tried to include one such question in each set of exercises—and it is good to see many examples of this type in these texts. But the arguments for a hurried introduction of a new subject seem far less compelling.

Inequalities are studied in depth in some countries. Certainly, the following Japanese exercise:

solve:

$$\frac{x-1}{5} - \frac{x}{3} > 2$$

is a testing question to ask of grade 8 students. More particularly, I was interested in the attention paid in the different texts to that notoriously tricky point, the effect of multiplying through an inequality by a negative number. The French ask students to experiment, much in the way of the Norwegian example quoted above, and then produce the result. One Japanese series recognizes this as a particular sticking point and attempts, by graphical means, to justify the kernel which it then emphasizes. The Netherlands text does not deal specifically with multiplication by a negative number, but its emphasis on doing the same to both sides of the inequality (as in equations) may well be storing up future trouble (if, in fact, the median student is ever asked, or ever wishes, to multiply through an inequality by a negative number). In general, however, and with the exception of some examples in the English text, the books examined did not appear to pay especial attention to those points in mathematics which research and teaching experience have shown to cause particular problems for students. Quite how best this should be done is, however, not obvious. Providing clear and expanded textual explanations may not be sufficient. It may be necessary explicitly to permit conflicts to arise in the students' minds, to allow them to make false generalizations—that multiplication makes bigger or that "doing the same to both sides" is always permissible—and then help them to resolve and reconcile their difficulties.

Geometry

Some years ago I was slightly perturbed when a reviewer referred to the treatment of geometry in a grade 9 book I had edited as "physics" rather than "mathematics." Later, when I came across a quotation from an altogether outstanding schoolteacher and textbook author, C.V. Durell (quoted in Griffiths and Howson, p. 202), to the effect that "the fundamental difference between school geometry and university geometry is that the former is a branch of physics and the latter a branch of mathematics," I began more clearly to see my position. By that time I had also encountered the work of such U.S. 1960s projects as the Secondary School Mathematics Curriculum Improvement Study and a geometry text written for African schools which somewhere about page 60 asked them to prove that a line segment had one and only one mid-point. Thus, it was clearly demonstrated to me that there were those who took the view that geometry at school could be a branch of mathematics.

The treatments in the books studied are all firmly in the physics tradition (although, perhaps, the French and Japanese texts might claim to be theoretical physics). Results are based, in the main, on measurement, observation, and experimentation. There are exercises in "local deduction," which in the case of the Japanese and French texts become an introduction to the concept of proof, but general axiom systems are not to be found. Instead, the French, for example, list those properties which are needed as a basis for "local," restricted work.

These two countries have slightly different approaches to the task. Both follow traditional paths in laying emphasis on triangles, but the French lay great stress on seeing a proof in terms of a flow diagram or schema, which leads from given properties to a final conclusion. (One of the spin-offs of technology is the use made in most of the texts of flow diagrams to illustrate procedures as well as arithmetical algorithms.) At grade 8, the emphasis is on supplying missing details to incomplete flow diagrams, rather than on actually devising a flow diagram for a proof. That students should be able to construct a proof is an aim for grade 9 work.

The introduction of proof results in two immediate problems:

1. How to justify the mathematician's desire for proof.

2. How to link those geometrical topics chosen to illustrate proof to real-world applications.

There is also a third, not insignificant problem: proof is cognitively a very difficult topic, which in the past was taught only to high-attaining students.

Both countries make some attempt to justify proof, but the results are not entirely convincing. However, this is not an easy task to accomplish. Again, whereas the arithmetic that has been learned can soon be put to use on contextualized tasks, there are not too many examples one can give of how, say, the concurrency of the altitudes of a triangle affects our daily life. This results in a marked change in both books, and particularly the French, which up to the introduction of proof provides a very rich diet of applications. Its questions remain varied and interesting, but are now less often set in context. (The

French appear to have trawled far and wide in search of exercise items and it is good to see, for example, acknowledgements to the Australian Mathematics Competition for some of them.)

It is difficult to assess how successful such approaches will be with students drawn from all levels of the ability range. A Japanese mathematics educator, and a contributor to one of the series studied, estimated that some 30% to 40% of Japanese pupils would, at the end of grade 8, be capable of writing out a proof in the desired manner. This, based on experience in selective English grammar schools, would seem a remarkable achievement on the part of Japanese teachers. However, it does mean that the majority of the class will not attain the desired operational goals of the teaching. A similar position existed in the old Soviet Union with respect to the teaching to all of the differential and integral calculus. Then my question on the value of this to the many students who left school having understood little was answered: "but at least they all know there is such a subject and they have all been given the chance to learn it." Again, we are confronted with the conflict between separating students into clearly defined streams with their own curricula based on our preconceptions concerning ability, attainment, and aptitudes, but possibly at the expense of labelling many of them as inferior and denying them a true picture of what mathematics comprises; or, alternatively, of entering everyone for the mathematical equivalent of a two mile swim (and hard luck on the weak swimmers).

Away from the issue of proof, we notice other significant differences. Spain has hardly anything to say about geometry in its text, and Switzerland relatively little, although what it does do includes some good work on 3-D visualization. There is a growing recognition of the need to stress this aspect of geometrical work, particularly in the case of the average-attaining pupil. A similar need to be able to interpret maps and plans receives rather less attention at this level. Mensuration is stressed everywhere, but by this grade the countries have reached very different points in their progress through this topic. Perhaps attention should be drawn here to the way in which the French distinguish clearly between circle and disc, sphere and ball. In other texts such distinctions are not always made and, for example, the cir-

Table 3.3: Geometric Topics

Topic	E	F	J	Ne	No	Sw	U.S.
Area:							
rectangles and combinations	●			●	●		
Irregular shapes (squared paper)	●						●
Triangles and parallelograms			●	●	●	●	
Circles	●			●	●		
Surface area:							
sphere		●					○
cylinder					●		●
Volume:							
balls (spheres)		●					
cubes, prisms, cylinders					●		●
Angles:							
degree, measure	●			●	●		●
of n-gons			●				
Ruler and compasses work	●	●	●	●	●	●	●
Plans and maps	●				●		
3-D visualization	●	○		●	○	●	●
Axial and point symmetry	●	●				●	●
Enlargements	●		●	●			●
Rotations and translations		●					●
Congruence (SSS,...)			●				○
Similarity			●	●			
Properties of:							
circles	○	●			○		
parallelograms (angles, etc.)		●	●				
spheres and balls		●					
triangles (concurrency, etc.)		●	●				
Projections		●					
Pythagoras		●			●		●
Trigonometry: cosines only		●					
sine, cos tan (acute)							●

E (England), F (France), J (Japan), Ne (Netherlands), No (Norway), Sw (Switzerland), U.S. (United States)

● Topics covered   ○ Topics only lightly covered

Note: Spain does not treat geometry in this grade.

33 *Cercle et médiatrice*

Sur un cercle '*ℓ* de centre O et de rayon *r*, on choisit trois points A, B et C tels que AB = BC = *r*.
Voici le schéma d'une démonstration qui permet de conclure que la corde (AC) est perpendiculaire
au rayon [OB] et passe par son milieu.

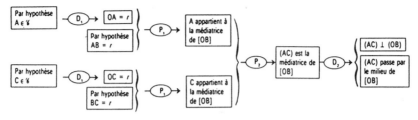

a) Faire une figure.
b) Énoncer les outils D_1, D_2, P_1 et P_2 qui interviennent dans cette démonstration.

The French textbook, Pythagore 4e, *includes this innovative approach to the teaching of proof.*

cumference of a circle may well mean a number or a geometrical locus. Again, we are faced with a key pedagogical problem. Part of the strength of mathematics is the flexibility of its language, which, as Bourbaki realized, one is forced to abuse from time to time. Nevertheless, the question remains, as in the case of percentages referred to earlier: where should we draw the pedagogical line, and where can relaxations be made without confusing and/or misleading students?

There is a general emphasis on transformation geometry, especially if one extends the definition of this to mean thinking of geometry and geometrical objects in dynamical terms. Work with ruler and compasses is also to be found in all texts. Japan makes considerable use of congruence and similarity but is almost alone in introducing these notions formally at this stage.

Pythagoras is treated by the French, the Dutch, and in the U.S. All use dissections of the square to justify the theorem, the French doing this in a slightly more formal and directed manner. This theorem appears in grade 9 in Japan and, presumably, there, or later, in other countries.

The French include some work on orthogonal projections and this leads naturally into a definition of cosine for acute angles, the only trigonometric function it treats in grade 8. Already, though, this permits, for example, exercises on the lengths of parallels on the globe. The U.S. takes a more traditional path, introducing first tangent and then sine and cosine by means of ratios in a right angled triangle. Once again, the U.S. treatment is very concise and the number of exercises to aid retention is limited. One presumes that the next section on trigonometry will have to start again from the beginning. (Indeed, it would be an interesting piece of research to determine the recollections that different students have of this work when next they encounter it.) The French approach mirrors one used in England in the 1960s and which was later abandoned in favour of the traditional method. It would still seem to have advantages in preparing for a more general understanding of the trigonometric functions.

Probability and Statistics

Growing attention is now being paid to the presentation and interpretation of data. Spain omits this topic in grade 8 and the Netherlands do not make it a central teaching topic, although its text contains some relevant examples. France, Japan, Norway, and the U.S. go further than a first introduction and at this stage develop the ideas of frequency and histograms. The U.S. text, in a very interesting chapter, also introduces two more modern ways of illustrating data: stem and leaf plots and box and whisker diagrams. The U.S. alone deals with mode and median, although Japan and Norway introduce the notion of mean. Japan and the U.S. take a first look at correlation through the use of scatter diagrams. I was interested to see the topic of statistical indices introduced in the French texts. References to these can be found in any newspaper, yet they are rarely to be found in curricula. On the other hand, pictograms, which nowadays rarely feature in the media, still have a place in many syllabuses and provide a cautionary example of the way in which school mathematics can occasionally become detached from that of the world outside.

Switzerland and the U.S. pay considerable attention to combinatorics prior to introducing probabilistic notions. The U.S. formally introduces permutations and combinations, but the Swiss text contents itself with setting the problem "how many?" in a number of "network" and similar contexts.

England engages in experimental work in probability leading to

Table 3.4: Probability and Statistics Topics

Topic	E	F	J	No	Sw	U.S.
			Country			
Displaying and interpreting data	●	●	●	●	○	●
Stem and leaf						●
Box and whisker						●
Frequency and cumulative frequency		●	●	●		●
Histograms		●	●	●		●
Mean			●	●		●
Mode and median						●
Scatter diagrams			●			●
Indices		●				
Combinatorics (pre-probability)					●	●
Experimental probability (percentage likelihoods)	●					
0-1 scale probability					●	●
Combined probabilities (repeated trials)					●	●

E (England), F (France), J (Japan), No (Norway), Sw (Switzerland), U.S. (United States)

● Topics covered   ○Topics only lightly covered

Note: The Netherlands and Spain do not treat these topics specifically at this grade.

the plotting of likelihoods, obtained by observing frequencies, as percentages. Grade 9 students are told that "We often use *fractions* rather than percentages for probabilities..." and from then on conventional probability measures are used. Again, interesting pedagogical points are raised concerning changes in terminology and the introduction of alternative descriptions. It must be observed, however, that this approach allows for some review of simple percentages and that weather-forecasters on British TV have now taken to giving the probability of rain as a percentage. The Swiss and the U.S. use the 0-1 scale from the start. Both countries consider simple examples of combined probabilities—usually repeated trials of an event. However, the U.S. informally introduces the notion of independent and dependent events. The Swiss text sets only eight questions in total on probability, although a few are in several parts. They are interesting and well-designed, including, for example, a "Monte Carlo" example to see if a cat will catch a mouse, but the manner in which items increase rapidly in difficulty and their limited number cast doubt about their value as a sole pedagogical aid. (Indeed, this would seem a problem with the Swiss text. There would appear to be a clear need for the teacher to provide many more straightforward exercises from other sources.)

Integration with Other Disciplines

As we have already remarked, a feature of the texts in general is the imaginative way in which examples and exercises are set. The contexts of many are determined by the students' personal interests and geographical location. Almost of necessity, many have a day-to-day civic arithmetic bias (supermarket shopping, the reading of timetables, etc.). However, there are many attempts to build in links with other disciplines. References can be found to architecture, art, astronomy, biology, botany, chemistry, geography, and history, and these are to be welcomed, not only for what they bring to the learning of mathematics by illustrating how it is used in other disciplines, but also for the way in which it supports the learning of these subjects and develops the general education of students. The French attempts are particularly interesting, although every country supplies its own unique examples. The U.S. tries to partition exercises and work under a variety of headings: career connection, consumer connection, science connection, health connection, social studies connection, music connection, but I do not believe this to be wholly successful. First, some of the connections are tenuous, and, of course, it is not always possible to supply exercises under these headings for all topics. More importantly, it can be very restrictive. Thus, for example, scientific notation is introduced for large numbers under "social science" (population figures), and for small under "science" (wavelengths). In contrast, the French subtitle groups of exercises within a more general set as, for example, a little economics, a little physics, a little biology. Powers of ten, for example, are illustrated by examples on the metric system, colour codes for resistances (a very nice example on coding and decoding), Voyager 2 (space exploration, including astronomical data), dinosaurs, the genesis of the universe, history (Charlemagne, the invention of printing), politics (last presidential election), anthropology (fire and Cro-Magnon man), engineering (the permitted play on a car's cylinder), and biochemistry (dimensions of a virus). Questions are then set within contexts taken from economics, astronomy, oceanography, physics, and biology, as well as such combinatorial situations as the number of chess openings and the different combinations possible with Rubik's cube: an extremely rich diet.

This is not to say that the French take all possible opportunities presented to them. They could learn something from the English, say, about contexts drawing upon art and architecture (and even more in this area from some of the material produced in the 1970s and '80s by Emma Castelnuovo and her fellow workers in Italy). What is evident is the rich source of examples to be found in the whole range of texts and the great need for countries to make more use of this international pool of ideas. There are some marvellous ideas waiting to be borrowed and used.

All this, however, takes a very limited (if practicable) view of cross-curricular work. We have been talking only about references to other subjects which occur within mathematics teaching and which work to the advantage of all the subjects concerned. There is no indication from any of the texts that cross-curricular work extends further than this: that, for example, interdisciplinary work of the kind fostered in the 1920s by Dewey and others, or which was encouraged in post-revolutionary Russia, is still taking place. Whilst acknowledging the logistical and educational problems which such work causes, it is disappointing that nothing appears to be happening to bring more closely together the teaching of different subjects.

Mathematics and Society

A key question to be asked of any text is to what extent does it show mathematics as being embedded in, and a product of, society? Indeed, this question could well be subdivided into other, more specific ones. How does the text demonstrate mathematics being used in society? In culture? What has the text to say about the genesis of mathematical knowledge: about the history of mathematics and the motivation for mathematical thought and advance? Is mathematics demonstrated as a developing topic on which professionals are still working? Is its multicultural nature clearly illustrated? How are students' personal knowledge, experiences, and interests employed for educational, motivational, and other ends? Are specific attempts made to deal with problems of gender and ethnicity?

It would be interesting in the cases of those countries with differentiated streams to see how the answers to these questions would vary between the texts written for different types of pupils. For example, there would seem to be a danger that in the present Netherlands text, "realistic mathematics" could result in a rather drab day-to-day diet for low-ability students. Of course one wishes to build upon the student's experience, to use contexts which are "realistic" to them, but it is also a goal of education to extend that experience. Here, as we have seen, cross-curricular examples have much to contribute. In England, although there is not such a strong contextual bias towards "restricted" utilitarianism as in the corresponding Netherlands text, we note that, for example, there are fewer historical references in the texts used by the median student.

As hinted at earlier, the history of mathematics and the human aspects of it receive scant treatment. I cannot recall seeing the portrait of any mathematician later than Descartes (although Edgar Allan Poe's portrait is in the Spanish text). While looking through the textbooks gathered for the main study, I found one with not only a portrait of Galois, but also a page of text describing his life and work. This was an Iranian textbook. This example of the cross-cultural nature of mathematics (for the Islamic contribution to mathematics was similarly illustrated) could not be readily matched in the texts which have been discussed in this monograph, although, for example, the Japanese texts do contain a section on Chinese arithmetic, illustrating the history of mathematics in that country, and the French have passing references to, for example, Hindu and Arabic contributions to mathematics and culture.

Even when chances presented themselves, they were not always taken. Norway has quite a good exercise in which students are given birth and death dates of nine great scientists and mathematicians, together with (very) brief biographical notes, and then asked questions such as "who lived longest?" Not surprisingly, Abel is one of the three mathematicians (with Archimedes and Newton), but there is no later example, although Marie Curie, Kristine Bonnevie, Einstein, Faraday, and Rutherford bring the story of science more up-to-date (as well as demonstrating that there are women scientists). It is strange that a mathematics text should prove a better advertisement for science than for its own subject.

There is no serious treatment of the history of mathematics, then, to be found in any of the texts studied. This is not very surprising, for little has been attempted in this direction. Of the widely-used textbooks I have studied over the years, only the East German (DDR) series of the 1960s tackled this problem in a serious manner with well-written chapters on history in each of their texts. Other texts have adopted the Iranian approach with occasional display pages devoted to historical aspects. This is at least a gesture towards history, but I suspect that the cause would be better served by approaches which started by trying more consciously to set examples in a historical and social context. The French text and the English one for high-attainers demonstrate historical aspects of mathematics education by including pages from old texts. This is an interesting idea: it appears to work better in the French case because that draws upon a wider range of examples. Old texts were not only about bread-and-butter arithmetic! Some eighteenth-century English texts had chapters on "Recreational Mathematics" (usually drawing heavily on French sources) and I know at least one with sheets of cardboard bound in with the text having ready-perforated nets which allowed readers to construct simple three-dimensional geometrical models to illustrate the work. The French also get round the problem of out-of-date social data (such as those on the calls made on the Berne fire service, which date from 1981), a problem which besets any text which is to remain in print for some time, by occasionally using historical data, for example, on food and drink consumed in Paris in the year 1844—an example giving rise to many interesting social and dietary comparisons with today. (The major problem of the provision of up-to-date data-banks is, surely, one that can be solved through the use of modern technology.) One possible peg on which to hang social and historical links appeared almost wholly neglected. It must be accepted that stamp-collecting does not exercise the same appeal to teenagers that it once did, but only the Netherlands used a stamp to illustrate its work (a 1955 Greek stamp illustrating Pythagoras' theorem for a 3-4-5 triangle). In fact, there is a vast range of postage stamps illustrating our subject and those who have contributed to it (see, for example, Wussing and Remane [1989] or Robin Wilson's column in the *Mathematical Intelligencer*). Their use in texts would serve not only to draw attention to mathematics and mathematicians but, equally importantly, to the fact that countries have acknowledged the contributions made by them to society and its well being.

Since there is little emphasis on mathematics being the work of humans, then a key gender problem, that to date so much of mathematics is man-made, never arises. What we have are equal numbers of girls' names in the text and of girls in the illustrations. There may still be a bias towards the interests of boys in the choice of contexts, but, even if this is the case, it is not as pronounced as it was in certain 1960s texts. Again, though, what we have, as in the case of ethnicity, is an emphasis on neutrality: not on setting out deliberately to engage the interest of girls or ethnic minorities and to attract more of them to mathematics. Norway is by no means alone in concealing the existence of *women* mathematicians.

In general, then, one notes advances in attempts to place mathematics within a social context, but these are only the first steps towards the solution of a major problem. Moreover, it is not clear that very much further progress can be made along the paths currently being pursued. While it is necessary to consolidate and retain such gains as have been made and, again, to consider what is being done in other countries and to adapt and utilize their ideas, there is also a need to consider new approaches to the problem. Some of these may well be incompatible with the culture of the "textbook" and will require either some other form of media input, or a greater contribution from the teacher. Yet it would seem essential that texts do present a more rounded view of mathematics and that "innovation" and "attraction" should not merely refer to developments in the colourful packaging and presentation of traditional material.

Notes

[1] Only in 1988 was legislation passed decreeing that England should have a national curriculum in mathematics. Since then efforts have clearly been made to make up for lost time. A first version was in use by 1990 and this was revised in 1992. All the quotations are from this 1992 version. However, in 1994 it was decided to revise the curriculum yet again, and a new version was published in November 1994. It is proposed that this should have a shelf life of "at least five years."

[2] The use of exercises to carry covert political and social statements also has a long history. Thus, for example, Recorde's *Ground* has an example gently mocking the established church. In the second edition he introduced an exercise on the vexed political question of sheep and enclosures. Social pressures on authors are exhibited in his *Castle of Knowledge*, a book on astronomy, which skirts delicately around the contemporary religious controversy of heliocentricity. See, for example, Howson (1982), Easton (1967), Kaplan (1960).

[3] A deeper discussion of the ways in which operations on the integers are defined in the various texts will appear as part of a chapter to be published in a collection of papers contributed by members of the BACOMET group which should appear in late 1995 or early 1996.

[4] A witch has two types of cubes which she can put in her cauldron. One, let us call them black, raises the temperature by one degree celsius; the other, red, lowers the temperature by one degree. These then act as vectors and can be added and subtracted. Scientific principles become a little more strained when it is decided that it is permissible to take out a cube from the cauldron. Taking out a red cube will raise the temperature by one degree. Since we are denied the opportunity to multiply one red cube by another, multiplication is effectively defined by grouping cubes and studying the effects; the model is based, in other words, on the scalar multiplication of vectors and effectively defines a vector space—not the algebraic structure required. It should, in fairness, be pointed out that, possibly in an attempt to make amends, the authors do include a very interesting page devoted to the topic of

temperature (albeit, in an earlier chapter and associated with exercises on formulae for converting between different temperature scales). This mentions Lord Kelvin's description of absolute zero (thus raising the unstated problem of just how many red cubes the witch might be allowed to have) and of recent attempts by physicists to approach this (and so illustrating that *science* is still a living subject).

Chapter 4

Some Conclusions

My aim in carrying out this study was not to produce a list of texts in order of merit, or even to establish which, in my view, was the best buy. Indeed, it is important to realize that even if prizes were to be awarded then this would have to be done under many different headings: for example, mathematical and linguistic accuracy; clarity of mathematical presentation; the range of teaching and learning opportunities presented; philosophical and pedagogical coherence and soundness; the use of typography and illustrations to convey mathematical messages and emphases. Rather, I treated the study as a voyage of discovery. What trends were discernible? What were the most marked differences? To what extent did aims and expectations appear to differ? In which areas would further research seem most desirable? Again, the list could be extended.

The most obvious differences between these texts and those to be found thirty years ago are the increased emphasis on contextualizing examples and exercises (and, in some texts, on building bridges with other disciplines), and the use of new technological tools such as the calculator and the microcomputer. Also, considerably greater weight is placed on statistics and probability.

These moves are to be welcomed. However, in the first two cases, there would appear to be some worrying tendencies and consequences.

Basing mathematics teaching on utilitarianism and treating mathematics as commonsense, or a mere extension of this, may well create problems for those who wish to proceed further with the subject. The needs to prove, abstract, and generalize will not be readily appreciated, and those conflicts which arose historically between mathematics and commonsense (the multiplication of negative numbers and those associated with infinite sets, for example) may well create major teaching hurdles. (These problems are considered in more detail in the collection of papers described in note 3 in chapter 3.)

So little use is made in these texts of the microcomputer that it is almost premature to comment. Paradoxically, it is the French approach, based on writing simple programs, that perhaps offers more in terms of encouraging the development of desirable mathematical traits. It asks for a clear appreciation and analysis of the problem to be tackled and a methodical, precisely written approach to its solution. It discourages taking refuge in black boxes. Yet the use of prepared software offers far greater opportunities to introduce new insights on, and develop new approaches to, mathematical content. The temptation to squander these opportunities on examples which lack clear mathematical point must be resisted. However, what must also be considered are the losses which might occur as a result of using the calculator or prepared software. So much of the argument concerning the introduction of calculators has centred around their possible effects on students' arithmetical competence that other significant changes have been ignored. Of course, for example, one gains in time, ease, and accuracy when using a calculator rather than paper and pencil methods, a slide-rule, or a set of trigonometric tables. But what is lost, say, in the acquisition of fluency in the algebraic manipulation of arithmetical terms and the ability to estimate, or in the appreciation of logarithms and functions in general? (The introduction to our classrooms of graphical calculators will offer both new opportunities and challenges.) Earlier, I mentioned the analogous problems which arose in the teaching of geometry when algebraic methods were first introduced into schools and universities. Let us hope that we can do better than our predecessors in identifying and ameliorating possible problems.

On the other hand, what is not readily identifiable in the 1990s texts is any marked attempt to provide a clear structure for school mathematics. This was tried in the 1960s but failed because of the abstract and algebraic nature of the structure used. Yet, nowadays, few attempts are made to supply students with any framework to which they can relate their mathematics learning or which will enable them to comprehend the inter-relationships of the topics studied. There is a resulting danger that mathematics will appear a somewhat random collection of results and techniques.

As we have seen, with the exceptions of the Swiss and English texts, very similar assumptions are made about how teachers will organize their lessons. The English, French, and U.S. texts go further than most in offering a wider range of learning situations, should the teacher wish to take advantage of these. This increased choice, even if still limited, must be welcomed. One fears that in many classrooms these opportunities will not be grasped. Nevertheless, this approach may ultimately prove a more successful means of implementing change than would an outright attempt to revolutionize teaching methods in the classroom (which would inevitably have to be undertaken with insufficient resources for teacher [re]education and could easily lead to total rejection—the fate of many 1960s innovations still having much to offer). The English text would, to me, make unwarrantable assumptions about the value of well-planned activities divorced from clear statements of kernels intended to help students identify key results to be noted or memorized. The Swiss teacher is given the responsibility of developing kernels in class discussion. Again, if this opportunity is not taken, or not done well, then students will effectively be asked to determine for themselves what is important and what will be used again (a difficult task if carried out without the aid of a crystal ball) and what is transitory and inconsequential. The inclusion in a text of an index or, better still, a glossary is a philosophical statement about the nature of mathematical knowledge and the learning of mathematics.

The reader will be aware that I believe most texts give a very limited view of the nature of mathematics: of its history and multicultural origins, and of its existence as a living and expanding discipline dependent on human endeavour and on two main driving forces—the solution of societal problems and the meeting of intellectual challenges. What meaning will students attach to "doing mathematics" or "being a mathematician"? It could be argued that grade 8 is too early to be bothered with such considerations. I cannot agree. Many students will be nearing the end of their compulsory mathematics courses. They will be in great danger of having studied mathematics for many years without being introduced to the meaning it can have outside "school mathematics." Others will be preparing to elect to study mathematics further without any clear idea of what that means. It is about this stage of education that attempts should begin to clarify such matters. Only the French convinced me of their recognition of the need both to provide this type of "meaning" and to seek to establish clear relationships between seemingly disjointed topics in mathematics.

Significantly, the French text offers this view of mathematics to all students. In those countries which offer differentiated texts, mathematics for the lower-ability pupils firmly emphasizes utilitarian aims and the acquisition of basic "numeracy." The arguments for and against differentiation are not primarily mathematical ones. Certainly, teaching a homogeneous class is easier than teaching one of mixed ability. Yet several countries appear to cope successfully with the latter form of organization. The arguments are to a considerable degree based on social factors and on what the educational system most urgently seeks: crudely, whether emphasis should be placed on ensuring that the abilities of the most able are developed as far as possible, or on seeking social homogeneity and the greatest overall "yield" for the system.

The fact that the textbooks were written for different target populations makes comparisons of standards difficult. Also, it must be realized that the more difficult exercises in a text may be attempted by few, if any, students. What is immediately noticeable from the tables of chapter 3 is the encyclopaedic nature of the U.S. text. This is in marked contrast to the books from Japan, Spain, and Switzerland. But no one pupil will attempt everything in the U.S. text, whereas in Japan we can be sure that the vast majority of students will study all the chapters in the book.

Similar equivocal remarks must be made concerning expectations on pupil attainment. For example, many of the U.S. exercises are extremely demanding, both of thought and technique, but the number of exercises—the bulk of which are very straightforward—is so great that we know that any student will only attempt a selection of them, which might, in practice, do little to stretch the mind. The Japanese are more demanding so far as content is concerned and also ask for more well-developed techniques. There are, however, observable differences between the three texts studied: all cover the same topics but they differ in the degree of technical ability expected. Again, the English median students follow a somewhat wider curriculum than students in the lower half of the ability range in the Netherlands and Switzerland, but less seems to be demanded from them in the way of technical mastery.

The test of good teaching and learning, however, is not what topics or exercises students have been exposed to, or what can be found in their texts, but rather what they leave the class understanding, feeling, and able to do. The TIMSS attainment tests and student questionnaires have been specifically designed to throw light on such matters. This present small study will have succeeded if it helps in the interpretation of those TIMSS data: if it alerts its readers to the many factors which have to be taken into account when trying to account for those national differences which the TIMSS data will highlight.

References

Bell, A., Crust, R., Shannon, A., and Swan, M. (1993). *Awareness of Learning, Reflection and Transfer in School Mathematics: Teachers' Handbook.* Nottingham: Shell Centre.

Ben-Peretz, M. (1990). *The Teacher-Curriculum Encounter: Freeing Teachers from the Tyranny of Texts.* Albany: SUNY Press.

Clairaut, A.C. *Elements of Geometry.* (1881). (Trans. J. Kaines). London: Kegan Paul.

Cockroft, W.H. (Chair of Committee). (1982). *Mathematics Counts.* London: Her Majesty's Stationery Office.

Davis, R.B. (1992). Reflections on Where Mathematics Education Now Stands and on Where It May Be Going. In Grouws, op. cit., 724-734.

Dormolen, J. van. (1986). Textual Analysis. In Christiansen, B., Howson, A.G., and Otte, M. (Eds.). *Perspectives on Mathematics Education.* 141-171. Dordrecht: Reidel.

Dowling, P. (1991). A Touch of Class: Ability, Social Class and Intertext in *SMP 11-16.* In Pimm, D. and Love, E. (Eds.), *Teaching and Learning School Mathematics*, 137-152. London: Hodder and Stoughton.

Easton, J.B. (1967). The Early Editions of Robert Recorde's *Ground of Artes. Isis*, 58, 515-532.

Ernest, P. (1991). *The Philosophy of Mathematics Education.* Basingstoke: Falmer Press.

Freudenthal, H. (1975). Pupil's Achievement Internationally Compared—the IEA. *Educational Studies in Mathematics,* 6, 127-186.

Gardiner, A. (1992). *Recurring Themes in School Mathematics.* Birmingham University: UK Mathematics Foundation.

Glaeser, G. (1984). A propos de la pédagogie de Clairaut. *Recherches en Didactique des Mathématiques,* 4, 332-340.

Goffree, F. (1985). The Teacher and Curriculum Development. *For the Learning of Mathematics,* 5, 26-27.

Gravemeijer, K.P.E. (1994). *Developing Realistic Mathematics Education.* Utrecht: Freudenthal Institute.

Griffiths, H.B. and Howson, A.G. (1974). *Mathematics: Society and Curricula.* Cambridge: Cambridge University Press.

Grouws, D.A. (1992). *Handbook of Research on Mathematics Teaching and Learning.* New York: Macmillan.

Howson, A.G. (1982). *A History of Mathematics Education in England.* Cambridge: Cambridge University Press.

———. (1989). Applications in the History of Mathematics Teaching. *Llull,* 12, 365-395.

———. (1991). *National Curricula in Mathematics.* Leicester: The Mathematical Association.

———. (1993). Review of "Pimm, D. and Love, E. (Eds.). *Teaching School Mathematics." Zentralblatt für Didaktik der Mathematik.* 2, 57-59.

Howson, A.G., Keitel, C., and Kilpatrick, J. (1981). *Curriculum Development in Mathematics.* Cambridge: Cambridge University Press.

Howson, A.G. (Ed.). (1987). *Challenges and Responses in Mathematics.* Cambridge: Cambridge University Press.

Jahnke, H.N. (1994). Cultural Influences on Mathematics Teaching. In Biehler, R., Scholz, R.W., Strässer, R., and Winkelmann, B. (Eds.), *Didactics of Mathematics as a Scientific Discipline,* 415-429. Dordrecht: Kluwer.

Kaplan, E. (1960). *Robert Recorde: Studies in the Life and Works of a Tudor Scientist.* PhD dissertation, New York University

Keitel, C. (1987). A Glance at *SMP 11-16* from a Distance. In Howson (1987), 67-74.

Keitel, C., Otte, M., and Seeger, F. (1980). *Text-Wissen-Tätigkeit: Das Schulbuch in Mathematikunterricht.* Königstein/Ts.

Laborde, C. (1994). Enseigner la géométrie: permanences et révolutions. In Gaulin, G., Hodgson, B.R., Wheeler, D.H., and Egsgard, J.C. (Eds.), *Proceedings of the 7th International Congress on Mathematical Education,* 47-75. Quebec: Laval University Press.

Lakatos, I. (1976). *Proofs and Refutations.* Cambridge: Cambridge University Press.

McKnight, C.C., Crosswhite, F.J., Dossey, J.A., Kifer, E., Swafford,

J.O., Travers, K.J., and Cooney, T.J. (1987). *The Underachieving Curriculum*. Champaign, Illinois: Stipes Publishing.

Ministère de l'Education Nationale. (1994). *Repères et Référénces Statistiques*. Paris.

Morgan, J. (1977). *Affective Consequences for the Learning and Teaching of Mathematics of an Individualised Learning Programme*. Stirling: DIME.

National Council of Teachers of Mathematics (1989). *Curriculum and Evaluation Standards for School Mathematics*. Reston, VA: NCTM.

Otte, M. (1986). What Is a Text? In Christiansen, B., Howson, A.G., and Otte, M. (Eds.), *Perspectives on Mathematics Education*, 173-204. Dordrecht: Reidel.

Pimm, D. (1987). *Speaking Mathematically*. New York: Routledge and Kegan Paul.

Recorde, R. (1543). *The Ground of Artes*. (Facsimile edition published in English Experience Series).

Ries, A. (1574 edition). *Rechenbuch*. (Facsimile edition, 1992, Hannover: Verlag Th. Schäfer).

Secada, W.G. (1992). Race, Ethnicity, Social Class, Language, and Achievement in Mathematics. In Grouws, op. cit., 623-660.

Shuard, H. and Rothery, A. (1983). *Children Reading Mathematics*. London: Murray.

Stevenson, H.W., Lee, S., and Stigler, J. (1986). Mathematics Achievement of Chinese, Japanese and American children. *Science,* 231, 693-699.

Thom, R. (1972). Modern Mathematics: Does It Really Exist? In Howson, A.G. (Ed.), *Developments in Mathematical Education*, 194-209. Cambridge: Cambridge University Press.

Travers, K.J. and Westbury, I. (1989). *The IEA Study of Mathematics I: Analysis of Mathematical Curricula*. Oxford: Pergamon Press.

Wirszup, I. (1981). The Soviet Challenge. *Educational Leadership*. 38(5).

Wussing, H. and Remane, H. (1989). *Wissenschaftsgeschichte en miniature*. Berlin: VEB Deutscher Verlag der Wissenschaften.

Index

Copyright Permissions

Every effort has been made to acknowledge all sources of material used in this book. The publishers would be grateful if any errors or omissions were pointed out, so that they may be corrected.

Acknowledgement is gratefully made for the use of the following copyright material:

Page 18: diagram on p. 147, *Chugaku Sugaku*, reprinted by permission of Osaka Shoseki, Inc.
Page 40: "Impossible Objects" from p. 36, *SMP11-16 B2*, reprinted by permission of Cambridge University Press.
Page 76: Exercise 33 from p. 134, *Pythagore 4e*, reprinted by permission of Librairie Hatier SA.